(64 - 11734) 6-30-65

Rutherford and the Nature of the Atom

EDWARD NEVILLE DA COSTA ANDRADE was one of the chosen band who worked under "Papa" Rutherford at the University of Manchester, in England, when Rutherford, with no more equipment than odds and ends of apparatus worth a few thousand dollars at most, showed the world how to put together the experimental foundation of our atomic and nuclear age. To this task of biography Professor Andrade thus could bring fond personal recollections, along with a scientist's understanding, a historian's eye for perspective, and a practiced writer's passion for clarity.

Now Senior Research Fellow of the Department of Metallurgy, Imperial College of Science, London, Professor Andrade throughout his professional career has kept one foot planted in each of the supposedly antithetical "Two Cultures," of which we have heard so much in recent years. Among his fellow physicists he is known for fundamental investigations concerning the creep of metals, including his law of creep; for work on the viscosity of liquids, including his law of the variation of viscosity with temperature and the establishment of the effect of an electric field on the viscosity of liquids; for discoveries relating to sound; and for the work which he did with Rutherford on the wave length of gamma rays. At the other end of the range of his talents he has impressed discriminating readers on both sides of the Atlantic with the elegant austerity of his prose in the short biography of Sir Isaac Newton which appeared in 1954 and now is often cited as the best introduction to Newton and his discoveries. As chairman of the Royal Society's committee dealing with the publication of Newton's correspondence, Andrade is one of the acknowledged experts on that great man, as indeed he is on Robert Hooke, and he is the Honorary Librarian of the Royal Society. London audiences know him as a gifted and sympathetic lecturer on science; he was a popular member of the BBC's Brains Trust in World War II days and after; and he has delivered three of the celebrated series of Christmas Lectures of the Royal Institution, of which he was Director in 1950–52. Varied though it is, this recitation of accomplishment does not complete the picture, for Andrade also is a poet and a man of the world whose witticisms (frequently caustic) are treasured by friends on both sides of the English Channel. A book of his verse was published in 1924, and another book, including some of the earlier poems, in 1949. In one period he wrote a column on food and wine for *The London Mercury,* a literary magazine. He was a close friend of famous writers, H. G. Wells, Hilaire Belloc, and Walter de la Mare among them.

Of English-Portuguese descent (the family moved to England in the Napoleonic era), Andrade was born in London on December 27, 1887. At eleven he entered St. Dunstan's College, whose headmaster had an interest in science unusual for those days, and there had an introduction to the laboratory. Good teachers at University College, London, fanned Andrade's curiosity about physics (when he was not winning the half-mile, the lightweight boxing championship, and playing rugby and cricket), and he took his degree, B.Sc., with first-class honors in physics at the age of nineteen. Professor Frederick Trouton encouraged him to do research in physics; at twenty-two Andrade published his now classical law of creep.

In 1910 Andrade went to Heidelberg on a scholarship and worked under Philipp Lenard, a Nobel Laureate, on the electrical properties of flames. He received the Ph.D. degree, *summa cum laude,* and after a year at the Cavendish Laboratory (at Cambridge University) and a year at University College, he joined Rutherford at Manchester for the great experience that led to the writing of this book. At the outbreak of World War I Andrade joined the Royal Artillery. He saw active service at the front in France for two and a half years, beginning in February 1915, where, however, since he did not carry a sword, he had little opportunity of displaying that he had taken full advantage of his training for the front in England, which had "consisted of learning to salute with a sword on horseback." However, he attained the rank of captain and received mention in dispatches.

After the war Andrade was Professor of Physics at the Woolwich Artillery College, now the Military College of Science, until 1928, when he returned to University College as Quain Professor of Physics, the Quain being the senior physics professorship in the University of London. In World War II he was, among other things, Scientific Adviser to the Director of Research at the Ministry of Supply. He retired as Quain Professor in 1950 when appointed Director of the Royal Institution, some years later assuming the research fellowship at the Imperial College of Science.

Professor Andrade's publications include:

The Structure of the Atom. 1923 (G. Bell: Harcourt Brace). Third edition, revised, 1927, and subsequent editions. For some years the standard book in English on the subject.

Engines. 1928 (G. Bell: Harcourt Brace). Translated into Polish. Went into many editions. A book for the general reader, founded on Christmas lectures given at the Royal Institution.

The Mechanism of Nature. 1930 (G. Bell: Lippincott). Translated into French, Italian, Polish, Dutch, Danish, and Swedish. Went into many English editions. A simple account of modern views of the structure of matter and radiation.

The Atom and Its Energy. 1947 (G. Bell). A simple account of atomic structure, leading to the atomic bomb.

An Hour of Physics. 1930 (Lippincott).

An Approach to Modern Physics. 1956 (G. Bell: Doubleday). Third edition 1962. Translated into Italian and Dutch.

Sir Isaac Newton. 1954 (Collins: Doubleday). Later editions.

A Brief History of the Royal Society. 1960 (The Royal Society). Published on the occasion of the 300th anniversary of the foundation of the Society.

Poems and Songs. 1949 (Macmillan).

Over the years many honors have come to Professor Andrade. He gave the Guthrie Lecture to the Physical Society and the James Forest Lecture to the Institution of Civil Engineers in 1941, the Wilkins Lecture of the Royal Society in 1949, and the Rutherford Memorial Lecture of the Royal Society in 1957. He has been on the Council of the Royal Society, President of the Physical Society, Holweck Prizeman and recipient of the Hughes Medal of the Royal Society and of the Grande Médaille Osmond of the French Society of Metallurgy. His reputation is high in France; he is a

Chevalier of the Legion of Honor, a Membre d'Honneur of the French Physical Society, and Membre Correspondant de l'Académie des Sciences, Institut de France.

John H. Durston

Rutherford and the Nature of the Atom

BY E. N. DA C. ANDRADE

Published by Anchor Books

Doubleday & Company, Inc.
Garden City, New York

Rutherford and
the Nature of the Atom

by E. N. da C. ANDRADE

Garden City, New York

THE SCIENCE STUDY SERIES

The Science Study Series offers to students and to the general public the writing of distinguished authors on the most stirring and fundamental topics of science, from the smallest known particles to the whole universe. Some of the books tell of the role of science in the world of man, his technology and civilization. Others are biographical in nature, telling the fascinating stories of the great discoverers and their discoveries. All the authors have been selected both for expertness in the fields they discuss and for ability to communicate their special knowledge and their own views in an interesting way. The primary purpose of these books is to provide a survey within the grasp of the young student or the layman. Many of the books, it is hoped, will encourage the reader to make his own investigations of natural phenomena.

The Series, which now offers topics in all the sciences and their applications, had its beginning in a project to revise the secondary schools' physics curriculum. At the Massachusetts Institute of Technology during 1956 a group of physicists, high school teachers, journalists, apparatus designers, film producers, and other specialists organized the Physical Science Study Committee, now operating as part of Educational Services Incorporated, Watertown, Massachusetts. They pooled their knowledge and experience toward the design and creation of aids to the learning of physics. Initially their effort was supported by the National Science Foundation, which has continued to aid the program. The Ford Foundation, the Fund for the Advancement of Education, and the Alfred P. Sloan Foundation have also given support. The Committee has created a textbook, an extensive film series, a laboratory guide, especially designed apparatus, and a teacher's source book.

The Series is guided by a Board of Editors consisting of Bruce F. Kingsbury, Managing Editor; John H. Durston, General Editor; Paul F. Brandwein, the Conservation Foundation and Harcourt, Brace & World, Inc.; Samuel A. Goudsmit, Brookhaven National Laboratory; Philippe LeCorbeiller, Harvard University; and Gerard Piel, *Scientific American*.

PREFACE

It has proved a great pleasure to comply with the suggestion made by Mr. Kingsbury that I should write a short life of Ernest Rutherford, the founder of modern atomic physics. To revive the memories of the time when the great man was in intimate touch with all those engaged on research in his laboratory, as Rutherford was at Manchester, is to recall conditions which have inevitably passed. To consider the earlier years, at the end of the past century, when Rutherford started his researches, is to contemplate a vanished era, for Benjamin Franklin, had he been miraculously transported to those days, would have found things less strange, less startling, than would a man of those days transported to the present time. It has been a refreshing task to write of those strangely distant times, which I vividly remember, and to try to present to the keen young generation of today a picture of what the pursuit of scientific discovery was like before it became a profession, and of a unique character in the glory of his early achievement.

After the First World War things had changed, but it was then that the wonderful work of Rutherford and his co-workers led to the first study of the structure of the nucleus, a study which dominates so much of modern physics. I have striven to communicate something of the excitement of the discoveries of those times.

I can only regret that nearly all my letters from Rutherford were lost when my laboratory was destroyed in 1941 by a bomb let fall during a German air raid on

London. Some of them, written on the spur of the moment, were very characteristic. I have, however, quoted from many of his published letters. Reading these is like hearing the man speak.

The chief purpose, perhaps, of a preface is to acknowledge gratefully help generously given. For information and suggestions on particular points, and in some cases for photographs, I am deeply indebted to Sir Edward Appleton, Professor P. M. S. Blackett, Sir John Cockcroft, Professor P. I. Dee, Professor Norman Feather, and Sir Neville Mott, all of whom worked in Rutherford's laboratory and knew him well. Sir George Thomson, son of J. J. Thomson, has generously come to my aid in certain matters concerning the Cavendish Laboratory, and Sir Frank Smith, a close friend of Rutherford's, has most kindly read through my manuscript and made helpful suggestions. Professor Bernard Cohen has kindly assisted me with references to the state of physics in the United States in Rutherford's early days. Mr. W. D. Sturch, Secretary of the Royal Commissioners for the Exhibition of 1851, has helped in matters concerning the Royal Commission; Professor N. C. Phillips, of the University of Canterbury, New Zealand, and Mr. T. S. Karetu and Mr. G. L. Keeble, of New Zealand House, have been good enough to supply information on New Zealand matters. Mr. C. G. Tilley, of the Cavendish Laboratory, has rendered great assistance in the matter of Cavendish photographs and records, and Mr. K. D. Vernon, librarian of the Royal Institution, has always been ready to hunt up scarce books for me. To all these my warmest thanks are due, as to Mr. Durston, of Educational Services Incorporated, who has read my manuscript with great care and made discriminating and helpful suggestions.

E. N. da C. Andrade

NOTE ON THE EXCHANGE VALUE OF
UNITED STATES AND BRITISH MONEY

Moneys paid in England are usually given in British pounds throughout the book. During Rutherford's lifetime the rate of exchange of United States and British money did not vary. One British pound was worth approximately five dollars—actually about 3 per cent less—so that multiplication of the number of pounds by five will give closely enough the equivalent value in dollars. It need scarcely be said that the purchasing power of both dollar and pound fell somewhat during the First World War and fell far more during and after the Second World War, while income tax increased. Before the First World War £1000 a year was sufficient to support a family in considerable comfort in England.

CONTENTS

tion with Soddy. The Nature of Alpha and
Gamma Radiations. The Theory of Radioactive
Disintegration. Election to the Royal Society.
The Bakerian Lecture on Radioactive Decay.
The Age of the Earth. Radioactivity of the
Earth and Atmosphere. The Rumford Medal
and the Silliman Lectures. The Alpha Particle.
Friendship with Otto Hahn. A Second Edition
of *Radio-activity*. Plans to Leave McGill.

Rutherford and the Nature of the Atom

Rutherford and the Nature of the Atom

Chapter I

THE WORLD OF RUTHERFORD'S YOUTH

We live in an atomic age, when the possibility of procuring energy from the transmutation of atoms holds out, on the one hand, a promise of easy prosperity and, on the other hand, of universal destruction. The structure of the atom, which little more than fifty years ago was, like the existence of life on the planets, a matter of occasional conjecture, is now the subject of study of thousands, or tens of thousands, of accomplished and highly trained men of science and a source of expense exceeding that of the maintenance of the world's armies and navies in the old days. All this derives directly from the work of Ernest Rutherford.

The great astronomer Arthur S. Eddington said that in 1911 Rutherford introduced the greatest change in our ideas of matter since the time of Democritus—and Democritus lived four hundred years before Christ. He was referring to Rutherford's theory, put forward in that year, that every atom consisted of a very small electrically charged core, in which practically all its mass was concentrated, surrounded by a structure of electrical particles. The core was called the nucleus. At the time the notion of an atomic nucleus seemed fantastic to many; today the structure of this incredibly minute nucleus is intensely studied in leading laboratories all over the world. It is one object of this book to show how Rutherford's researches on radioactivity led him inevitably to this nuclear conception and to indicate how, mainly under his inspiration, the study of atomic structure, of atomic transmutation, and of atomic energy developed to a point where the extraordinary advances of recent years were foreshadowed. Another object, of course, is to paint the living man and to give some notion of his character, his methods, his qualities, and his influence. It is, however, hard to understand the originality, the value, and the nature of a man's achievement without some notion of the conditions in which he lived, of the opinions and convictions that prevailed in the field in which he worked and, above all, of the surroundings in which he grew up. Especially is this true of a man like Rutherford, who began his career in a world completely different from that in which we now exist, but who spent the last years of his life in conditions so much closer to ours that we are apt to forget this difference.

THE WORLD IN THE 1890s

Let us glance at the world in the time of Rutherford's youth. He was born in New Zealand in 1871, in circumstances that will be described in the next chapter, and first came to England in 1895, at the age of twenty-four. In those days there were, of course, no motor cars: the streets were full of horse-drawn carriages and carts. The modern type of bicycle, with two equal wheels, had recently been introduced, and was called the "safety" bicycle in contrast to its predecessor, the "ordinary" bicycle with a front wheel some five feet in diameter and a very small rear wheel. The free wheel appeared in 1894, variable gears were still to come. Shops selling saddles and harness for riding horses were common. The possibility of aeroplanes was not taken seriously: Wilbur and Orville Wright did not begin their epoch-making work until 1900 and did not fly until 1908. So much for transport—a different and more leisurely age indeed.

As for the home, in the typical house there was no telephone: in the United States, where the telephone was invented and where its manufacture was most advanced, there was in 1895 about one telephone per 200 of the population. There were no refrigerators in private houses. The year 1895 is given as the one in which, in the United States, the canning of food began to be placed on a mechanical and mass-production basis, and here again in England things were not so far advanced —if the canning of food can be said to be an advance. Electric lighting in the home was quite exceptional: the metal filament lamp had not been invented. In fact, as late as 1904 Rutherford, in a letter to his mother about the Exposition at St. Louis, thought it worth while to write, "The illumination at night was very fine—all by electricity, of course." Street lighting in cities was by gas. Although, as will be discussed in the next chapter, the possibilities of sending signals by wireless waves over short distances, a matter of yards, had been demonstrated by Heinrich Hertz, an event of great scientific importance as proving the existence of the waves, wireless telegraphy was unknown. It was not until 1898 that Guglielmo Marconi took out his first patent. Needless to say, then, sound broadcasting and television were things undreamt of, even by the most daring prophets of coming wonders.

As regards science as an agent for entertainment, a very crude phonograph, with cylindrical records, had been invented by Thomas A. Edison, which was in many homes in the 1890s but gave, I can assure the reader, a very harsh and grating reproduction. The position may, perhaps, be represented by the following quotation from an English book, *Discoveries and Inventions of the Nineteenth Century,* published in 1896: "There is no reason but what, with a loud-speaking phonograph uttering an orator's very words and tones, while instantaneous photographs of his successive gestures and attitudes are projected on a screen, a true and lively impression of his eloquence might be conveyed centuries after his decease." Elsewhere in the same book is a brief account of a "kinetographic theatre." In 1894 a "kinetoscope parlour" had been opened in New York, for showing motion pictures, as a curiosity, but the development of the motion picture as a means of entertainment did not begin until a couple of years later, and it was not until well into the twentieth century that the production of films lasting for an hour or more, with named actors and actresses, began. The first motion picture theater, or "nickelodeon," was opened in 1905.

THE BEGINNING OF RESEARCH LABORATORIES

Thus the year 1895, in which Rutherford came to England, may be said to mark, as precisely as any one year can, the end of an old civilization, of an era in which applications of electricity and of science in general played little part in the daily life of the average citizen, and the beginning of a new era in which such applications were to become every year more significant.

A feature of this new era which has had a profound effect on the study of science was the rise of the great industrial and governmental research laboratories, which today provide profitable careers for the greater part of the university post-graduate students of physics.

In the 1890s such laboratories had scarcely made an appearance. Even in Germany, an early leader in applied research, although firms engaged in the production of chemicals, such as artificial dyestuffs, employed skilled men of science working in what were, for the time, well-equipped laboratories, there were few or no industrial laboratories for physics. In the United States research laboratories such as those of the Bell Telephone Company, Westinghouse, or Kodak, to name but a few of such mighty institutions, had not been founded, whereas today it is certain that there are far more men employed on research in the Bell Telephone Laboratories alone than were engaged in research on physical subjects in all the universities of the world—that is, in all the physics laboratories of the world—in Rutherford's youth. Even allowing amply for the depreciation in the purchasing power of the dollar, the money now spent on research in that laboratory must be many times that spent in the whole world on physical research at the end of the last century.

Robert Millikan, the great American physicist who was awarded the Nobel Prize in 1923 for his work on the electron, records in his autobiography that even in 1907 neither the American Telephone and Telegraph Company in New York nor the General Electric Company in Schenectady had made more than the barest beginnings in research. In England, certainly at the time when Rutherford was carrying out his early researches at Cambridge and probably many years later, physical research played so small a part in industry that no successful young university physicist ever contemplated an industrial career. The famous Cambridge physicist J. J. Thomson, who fathered the young Rutherford's researches and of whom much will accordingly be written later, said, with reference to those times,

"There were no Government institutions like the National Physical Laboratory for research, both in pure physics and for solving difficulties which manufacturers meet with in the course of their business. There were no laboratories for research in problems of importance to the army, navy or air force such as are now to be found. . . ." He goes on to refer to the fact that no great firms had research laboratories. This is not without importance for Rutherford's youth, since the rise of these great research laboratories has had its influence on the research outlook in all universities.

As for the universities, the conditions in the best British university research laboratories at the end of the past century would strike the present-day physicist as extraordinarily primitive, and according to Millikan the state of things in England at that time was considerably better than that which prevailed in America. He writes, "In American universities the recognition of our backwardness was just beginning in the early nineties to lead to vigorous efforts to improve the situation," and draws attention to the fact that the first American journal for physics, the *Physical Review,* made its appearance in 1893 and that the American Physical Society was not founded until six years later. In 1894 there were in Britain about six periodical publications dealing with physics, but not with physics alone, and four in the United States: in 1934 there were 13,494 scientific periodicals, covering all sciences, it is true, but this number must imply something well over a thousand dealing with different aspects of physics.

The Cavendish Laboratory at Cambridge, England, where Rutherford first made his name, was built at a cost of £8450 and opened in 1871 (which happens to be the year of Rutherford's birth), the great Clerk Maxwell, the first Cavendish professor, delivering the inaugural lecture. A few years earlier Maxwell had carried out his fundamental experiments on the viscosity of gases at different pressures and temperatures, of which all students of physics learn, in a large garret in the house that was his home, higher temperatures of the apparatus being created by heating the whole room with a large coal fire and steam from kettles and lower temperatures by cooling the room with quantities of ice. There was no question of ordering a thermostatically controlled enclosure in those days: there was nobody to order it from. The Cavendish Laboratory was enlarged in 1896, at a cost of £4000, which was considered to be a heavy expense. The extended building comprised a workshop, teaching laboratories, and space for some sixteen men to do research, under somewhat cramped conditions. C. G. Barkla's first experiments were, for instance, carried out in a cellar of the porter's lodge. The professor had a small room to himself!

These conditions may not sound very grand, but they represented a great advance on those prevailing before the Cavendish was built. J. J. Thomson himself has recorded that when he was at Owens College, Manchester, where in 1876 he carried out his first research, the only thing that could be called a physics laboratory was a room in which apparatus used for lecture experiments was stored. A. W. Porter, who in 1896 carried out early experiments on X-rays, tells that in 1890, at University College, London, he had to dismantle his research apparatus each week in order to make room for undergraduates, and then build it up again. But a little earlier things had been worse. Of the famous John Ambrose Fleming, the inventor of the electronic valve, it is written that in 1884 his reputation in the field of the newest electrical developments was such that he was invited to become the first professor of electrical engineering at

University College, London. When he had accepted, he found, as he wrote in his reminiscences, that the equipment consisted of a piece of chalk and a blackboard. Later he won from the college authorities a grant of £150 for apparatus and the use of a small room as a laboratory. Many more examples could be given of the primitive research facilities of the time.

PIONEER LABORATORY EQUIPMENT

The conditions under which the experimenter did his work were by no means easy. In general, he had to make his own apparatus. P. Lenard, famous for his early work on the electron, told me that he himself made his first induction coil, the apparatus then generally used to produce high potentials. This took him several weeks. Sir William Ramsay, the discoverer of the rare gases, made much of his apparatus for handling gases: he was a first-class glass blower. The pioneers in experimental physics mostly knew their way about the workshop.

Two very good reasons for making one's own apparatus were a notable shortage of money grants and a notable shortage of instrument makers. Speaking of 1896 and the years immediately following, J. J. Thomson records that the cost of researches done in his laboratory had to be paid for by the laboratory itself. "The only aid it could get from outside was from the Government grant of £4000 a year for research, which was administered by the Royal Society and had to suffice for the needs of all the sciences, so that there was not much available for any particular science." Since the laboratory was financed mainly by fees from students and examinations, there was not much money to spare. R. J. Strutt, later Lord Rayleigh, writing of these times, recalls discussing with J. J. Thomson whether a new form of electroscope for radioactive measurements was worth the £5 that was asked for it. Some research students made their own electroscopes.

Manufacturers of physical apparatus were, in any case, practically unknown. The British firm of Baird & Tatlock was established in London in 1894: the American firm Cenco (Central Scientific Company of America) was founded in 1889, but both were in a small way of business and mainly occupied with simple apparatus for routine measurements in a few branches of industry and for such schools and other establishments as taught any science. The supply of special instruments for research was not a lucrative undertaking: a very small demand by people reluctant to pay even a very small price does not stimulate expert production.

Let us see what kind of instruments the new physics born in the 1890s demanded, since it was with them that Rutherford worked. Firstly the induction coil, to which reference has already been made, for the production of what were then considered high potentials, a few hundred thousand volts. It was generally known as the Ruhmkorff coil, after the man who first made it. It consisted of a core of straight iron wires wound with a few layers of thick insulated wire, called the primary coil, upon which were wound many thousands of turns of fine insulated wire, the secondary coil. An automatic make-and-break of the current through the primary induced a high potential in the secondary. Such a coil is to be seen on the right of the photograph of J. J. Thomson, taken in 1900, with his hand on the switch (Plate IV). The leading article in a scientific journal of 1898 stated: "The possessor of a good induction coil made by our leading instrument-maker should cherish it as the violin player cherishes his Stradivarius or his Guarnerius."

These induction coils, described in all the textbooks of the physics at the beginning of the century, were to be found in every physics laboratory until 1914, when the First World War began. During the war the electronic valve and its possibilities became known, with far-reaching effects on the physics laboratory as well as on the science of light electrical engineering. High voltage transformers, with modern rectifiers, became the new source of high potential for laboratory purposes. It is typical that after the war new induction coils, which had been purchased by the British government, could be bought at about a thirtieth of their pre-war cost. So suddenly did they go out.

Another piece of apparatus in general use was the cylinder vacuum pump, of the type invented by Francis Hauksbee nearly two hundred years earlier. An advertisement of 1897, from a publication dealing with the newly discovered X-rays, is shown in Plate II: it depicts a particular pump in common use in the days of Rutherford's first researches in England. The Sprengel pump, there mentioned, and the Toepler pump, of a similar type, were widely used: with both of these pumps a bulb containing mercury had to be raised and lowered repeatedly by hand. These mercury pumps were cheap and created what was for the time a good vacuum, but it took the best part of a morning to produce it, and great care was needed if the top of the apparatus was not to be knocked off in the later stages of pumping.

Currents were supplied by galvanic cells, which needed frequent attention, or by accumulators, which needed periodic recharging. The advertisement shown in Plate III, from the same publication as Plate II, refers to such galvanic batteries and to induction coils as necessary for X-ray photography and shows an early X-ray tube, of the type used by Rutherford. For potentials of hundreds of volts there were batteries of very small accumulator cells, made up of large test tubes containing acid with inverted U-shaped lead strips connecting them, which the research student had to know how to handle.

H. R. Robinson, who worked with Rutherford before the First World War, when Hans Geiger was also in the laboratory, writes of such batteries, "I can still remember his [Geiger's] sorrow on handing over to me a battery of small accumulators that I needed for the electrostatic deflection of alpha particles. This was a battery of 2400 volts, made up of sixty banks, each of twenty lead accumulators of a well-known test-tube type. The test tubes were very fragile, and the whole design of the battery highly vulnerable. Before handing it over, Geiger delivered a little homily: I was never to touch the battery connections while I was standing on the concrete floor; I must always keep a dry wooden board to stand on while making adjustments, and I must always hold one hand firmly behind my back while touching any part of the battery, so that there could be no risk of a circuit being completed through my body. Before I had any chance of expressing surprise at, or gratitude for, his solicitude, he went on with complete solemnity and singleness of mind: 'You see, if you get a bad shock you may kick out before you realise what you are doing, and the Prof. would not like it if some of the cells got broken.'" This is a picture of the time.

Small currents were measured by galvanometers, the deflection of the moving coil or magnet, to which a small mirror was attached, being read by means of an oil lamp and scale. Still smaller currents were measured by the leakage of electric charge indicated by an electroscope or electrometer. One elaborate form was the quadrant electrometer, much used by Rutherford in his pioneering experiments, to which reference will be made in Chapter III. Here the deflection was measured by the usual mirror, lamp, and scale. Another type also much used was the gold-leaf electroscope, which existed in many forms, all depending upon the fact that a very thin gold leaf, of about one three-hundredth of the thickness of a cigarette paper, can be moved aside by an extremely minute force. In one form two strips of gold leaf hang in a close or touching position from an insulated metal rod: when the rod is electrically charged both the strips acquire a charge of the same sign and so repel one another, the amount of the repulsion indicating the charge. The movement of the leaves was measured by a low-powered microscope with an eyepiece scale: the electroscope, or electric viewer, then became an electrometer, or electric measurer. In another form, devised by C. T. R. Wilson, there was only one gold leaf hanging next to a metal plate, from which it was repelled when leaf and plate were given a charge. Rutherford wrote in 1906: "The gold-leaf electroscope has proved an accurate and reliable means of measurement, and has played a prominent part in the development of radioactivity."

These simple laboratories of past times have been discussed, and a few pieces of commonly used apparatus have been described, in order to give some notion of the conditions under which discoveries in physics of fundamental importance were made, up to the end of the past century. It must not be forgotten that these circumstances, which seem so primitive today, did not prevent men of genius from carrying out pioneering work that led to physics as we know it. To recall but a very few of the great discoveries of the past century in the field with which Rutherford was concerned, Humphry Davy founded electrochemistry; Michael Faraday discovered electromagnetic induction; Heinrich Hertz established the existence of wireless waves; Wilhelm Conrad Röntgen discovered X-rays; J. J. Thomson and his school demonstrated the existence and properties of the electron with the simplest, practically home-made apparatus, inferior to that to be found today in the ordinary school laboratory. F. W. Lanchester was a great investigator who founded modern automobile design and was the first to explain the aerodynamics of the aeroplane wing: it was no doubt with the thought of such discoveries in mind that he said, when as an old man he was being taken round a splendid new research laboratory, "Too much apparatus, not enough brains."

It is difficult to estimate the quality of a great experimental genius, to judge the brilliance and originality of his discoveries, without a clear image of the conditions under which he worked, which is why so much attention has been devoted to these circumstances. Understanding of the thought and the theories that prevailed at the time of his investigations is also necessary and these matters will be considered when Rutherford's great discoveries are discussed. What has been attempted in this chapter is to show something of the domestic and scientific world, the university and the laboratory as Rutherford knew them when he set out on his great journey into the unknown.

Chapter II

THE DAYS IN NEW ZEALAND

New Zealand is a group of islands lying in the South Pacific, the white inhabitants of which in 1871 numbered some 250,000, which is about a tenth of the present-day population. It was there in that year, on August 30, that Ernest Rutherford was born, the fourth child of what eventually became a large family, for there were twelve children in all, although only nine of them reached adult age. His birthplace was a small homestead in primitive surroundings, and when later the family moved to a larger abode the mode of living was still very simple. Rutherford's father was a farmer who was prepared to undertake any skilled handiwork for which, in a simple but growing community, need arose. For instance, at one time he acted as a wheelwright, a craft at which his own father had been proficient. Later he set up a flax mill and a rope walk—that is, a long covered stretch for the manufacture of rope—which prospered. The nearest town to Rutherford's boyhood home was Nelson, named after the great British admiral, which at that time boasted some 5500 inhabitants. These matters, which may seem trifling, are of some significance in Rutherford's life. The very simple surroundings in which he grew to manhood had a great influence on his character. He always remained an essentially simple man, who loved simple people and simple ways and lived a simple life. The great Niels Bohr said of him in 1932, at a banquet given in his honor, "If a single word could be used to describe so vigorous and many sided a personality, it would certainly be 'simplicity,'" a theme which he then proceeded to develop. Rutherford himself said in a speech made and recorded in 1931, when he was sixty years old, "I am always a believer in simplicity, being a simple man myself." Throughout his life he retained a great affection for the land of his birth. When, in 1931, he was made a baron, an honor which calls for the nomination in the title of a particular place with which the recipient has been closely associated, he chose to be named "Lord Rutherford of Nelson." He might easily, had it not been for the love of his homeland, have selected some better-known place with which he had been connected, such as Cambridge. The great British scientist Edgar Adrian duly chose to be Lord Adrian of Cambridge when he was created a baron in 1955.

SCHOOLING

It was at Nelson that Rutherford went to school, first of all to a primary school and later, at the age of sixteen, to Nelson College, which was run on the lines of an English public school or American private secondary school. He was a bright, active boy, like Newton fond of making models, especially of water wheels; ready for birds'-nesting or fishing when opportunity offered; a great reader of books of all kinds, and good, but not outstandingly good, at outdoor games. Like Newton, again, he was no precocious genius, but a promising boy, very good with his hands.

At Nelson College he collected prizes in many subjects, including mathematics, but at that time the experimental sciences, such as physics and chemistry, played little part in school education in any part of the world and there is no record of any achievement in those subjects. After three years at Nelson College he went, with a scholarship, to what took the place of a local university, Canterbury College, in the city of Christchurch. This was a much bigger place than Nelson: the population of the city itself was about 16,000, but an additional 32,000 lived in surrounding suburbs.

In 1890, when Rutherford became an undergraduate, Canterbury College was a very small institution, with seven professors and 150 matriculated students. Living was cheap: it is recorded that a good room with board and the quiet necessary for study could be had for fifteen shillings a week and luxurious quarters for a pound a week. Today there is a teaching staff of well over two hundred and some thirty-six hundred students. A building of galvanized iron some sixty feet long served as the laboratory for both physics and chemistry. An outstanding member of the staff there was Professor A. W. Bickerton, who had a great influence on the young Rutherford. He was about fifty years old in Rutherford's undergraduate days and, although his official title was professor of chemistry and physics—in those days one man could easily handle both subjects up to the standard required—his great interest was astronomy. He had already put forward a theory that stars were formed by the grazing collision of two cosmical masses in a manner which he discussed in many papers at great length, but without any particular support from observation or calculation. His speculations were not taken very seriously by the established astronomers, but he was one of those fervent eccentrics who often make a great impression on the young. Rutherford always retained an affection for him, did his best for him when he came to England in the early years of the century, and when he died in 1929 published a tribute to him which, referring to his work in New Zealand, contained the words, "His powers of popular exposition, his enthusiasm and versatility were of great value in promoting an interest in science in a young community." Bickerton was an eloquent advocate of research and no doubt did much to incline Rutherford's thoughts to a quest for the undiscovered. G. von Hevesy, writing to Rutherford in 1913, referred to "a former teacher of yours, Bickerton. He is a funny old chap and one of the comical figures you find at every congress." He then tells how the mayor of Leamington, talking to Bickerton by chance on the railway platform at that town, asked him if he was Sir Oliver, meaning Sir Oliver Lodge, a physicist at that time extremely well known in England. "Not so famous, but greater," came the prompt answer. "I will never forget this scene," adds Hevesy. Another professor, C. H. H. Cook, gave the young man a training in elementary mathematics which served him well in later life.

EARLY EXPERIMENTS ON ELECTRO-MAGNETIC WAVES

After taking his degree in 1893, Rutherford began experimental research in a small drafty cellar, known to the students, who used to hang their caps and coats there, as the "Den." The subject of his experiments was the magnetization of iron in a rapidly alternating magnetic field. In J. A. Fleming's book *The Alternate Current Transformer,* published in 1890, Rutherford had found an account of some experiments by Heinrich Hertz on the magnetic properties of iron under the influence of alternating current discharge. A few years earlier, in 1887 and 1888, Hertz had established the existence and elementary properties of electromagnetic waves, today popularly known as radio waves, produced by the spark discharge of a condenser, which, with a suitable self-induction, produced rapid oscillations. Needless to say, Hertz's discovery of the waves had caused a sensation in the scientific world and it was, no doubt, this that directed the young Rutherford's attention to rapidly alternating electromagnetic fields. Others, also quoted in Fleming's reminiscences, had worked on the magnetic properties of iron in such fields, with varying results, and it was left to Rutherford to clear up the subject.

The results of his work were published in two papers in the *Transactions of the New Zealand Institute* for 1894 and 1895. The contents of these volumes are divided under the headings "Zoology," "Botany," "Geology," and "Miscellaneous,"[1] Rutherford's papers appearing under "Miscellaneous." In each volume there is only one other paper, of a few pages, dealing in any way with physics, but Professor Bickerton has papers on "The Immortality of the Cosmos, Being an Attempt to Show That the Theory of Dissipation of Energy Is Limited to Finite Portions of Space" and on "Principles and Phenomena of Cosmic Impact." Rutherford was working in intellectual solitude so far as physics was concerned. Regarding the material conditions under which he was working, not only did he have to make all his apparatus but he had to start every day by preparing a battery of Grove cells as his source of electric current. The Grove cell consists of a plate of platinum in nitric acid and a zinc plate in sulphuric acid, the sulphuric being contained in a porous pot standing in the nitric. In Rutherford's own words, this preparation

[1] In the volume for 1895, a heading "Chemistry" is added under which there are three short and unpretentious papers.

"involved the cleaning and amalgamation [that is, coating with mercury] of the zinc plates and adding the necessary acids. . . . I found this battery of low internal resistance a very convenient means of obtaining substantial and steady currents, but after several hours' work, the battery showed obvious signs of exhaustion and accurate work with it was impossible." It is doubtful if a research worker today, who probably does not know what a Grove cell is, would consider this a very convenient means of obtaining a current.

Rutherford produced his oscillation by sparks from an induction coil or from a frictional electric machine, in conjunction with a circuit containing a condenser and a solenoid, as a tubular coil was called, of known self-inductance. In the first paper he reached definite and clearly expressed results of some importance at the time. He proved that iron is magnetic for frequencies of up to 500 million per second, the frequency being simply calculated from the capacity and self-induction of the circuit. He showed that with wire needles the residual magnetization was a surface effect and proved it by dissolving away in acid the surface layers, a method which also enabled him to measure how the magnetization varied with the depth. He further found that the action of the rapidly alternating field on needles already strongly magnetized was to diminish the magnetization, an effect which he afterward used to make a sensitive detector of electromagnetic waves. In his second paper he dealt with the delay of the magnetization in following the magnetizing force, an effect which he termed magnetic viscosity. This investigation involved devising and making an apparatus which measured time intervals down to a hundred thousandth of a second. Altogether these two papers, if they do not announce a genius, as Newton's first published papers did, show an experimenter of outstanding ability, able to pose and answer definite problems without either technical aid or apparatus other than that made by himself.

In his research years Rutherford took a lively part in a Science Society founded at Christchurch in 1891, of which he became Secretary in 1893. An entry in the minute book of the society in 1894 records his interest in electromagnetic waves, with the detection of which he was about to busy himself. "Mr. Rutherford then read his paper on electrical waves and oscillations, in which he dealt with oscillatory discharges in general, referring more particularly to the recent researches of Hertz and Tesla and their bearing on Maxwell's theory. The paper was very fully illustrated by experiments performed by Mr. Rutherford with the assistance of Mr. Page and Mr. Erskine, the most striking of the experiments being a reproduction on a small scale of Tesla's experiments on the rapidly alternating currents." Nikola Tesla, who was born and educated in Croatia, emigrated to America as a young man and in 1892 had produced very high frequency currents, of some millions of cycles per second, by means of a special transformer, which created great interest at the time. He was a great inventor and made a fortune in the rapidly growing electrical industry.

A Scholarship and the Opportunity to Come to England

This brings us up to 1895, when Rutherford was awarded the scholarship which enabled him to come to England. In this connection it must be explained that a Great Exhibition had been held in London in 1851, under the patronage and direction of Prince Albert, Queen Victoria's consort. This exhibition was attended by over six million visitors and was in every way an outstanding success. A Royal Commission, which is still in existence, had been appointed to organize and run the exhibition and, after it was over, was directed to apply the large resulting profits to promote scientific and artistic education. One result was the foundation of the great museums of science and art, and of famous colleges of science, art, and music, which flourish in South Kensington, a part of London very near Hyde Park, where the exhibition was held. The matter of particular interest here is the foundation of the well-known 1851 Exhibition Science Scholarships. The purpose of these scholarships was to enable students who had given evidence of capacity for original research to continue their investigations. Recommendations for the awards, which normally ran for two years and sometimes a third, were made by certain universities and colleges named by the commissioners. The successful candidate was required to continue his work in some other institution than that by which he had been nominated. These scholarships, much sought after, are still in existence and have been held by some of the most famous men in British science, including two past presidents of the Royal Society, Rutherford himself and the great organic chemist Sir Robert Robinson, and eight winners of the Nobel Prize.

The commissioners decided to award such research scholarships to overseas students, as well as to students resident in Great Britain, and a scholarship was accordingly granted every second year to the most promising New Zealand student engaged on any branch of scientific research, to enable him to work in a university outside his own country. The award for 1895 was duly made to J. C. Maclaurin, a chemist who later became the New Zealand Dominion Analyst. He, however, for family reasons did not take up the scholarship, and it was then conferred on Rutherford. It was thus by lucky chance that Rutherford was able to come to England in 1895, although he had to borrow money to pay for his passage. Bickerton strongly supported Rutherford in a testimonial which contains the words "Mr. Rutherford has great fertility of resource, a very full acquaintance with both the analytical and graphic methods of mathematics and a full knowledge of the recent advances in electrical science and methods of absolute measurements. Personally Mr. Rutherford is of so kindly a disposition and so willing to help other students over their difficulties that he has endeared himself to all who have been brought into contact with him. We all most heartily wish him as successful a career in England as he has had in New Zealand." The wish was fulfilled.

Chapter III

THE CAVENDISH LABORATORY, CAMBRIDGE

Just before Rutherford left New Zealand he had managed to transmit Hertzian waves from one end to the other of the tin shed that served as the general laboratory for physics and chemistry and he intended to continue working on these waves and on their detection by the demagnetization effect that he had discovered.

He had determined to work if possible in the Cavendish Laboratory at Cambridge, which since 1884 had been under the direction of the famous J. J. Thomson, appointed to the post at the early age of twenty-eight. In 1893 Thomson had published a book very celebrated in its time, called *Recent Researches in Electricity and Magnetism*. It was in part a critical account of the work of others, in part of original work by himself. In particular it contained a lengthy chapter on the "Discharge of Electricity through Gases," describing many of his own investigations, which foreshadowed the work destined to be particularly associated with his name in the history of physics, and another lengthy chapter on electromagnetic waves, with which Rutherford must have been familiar. The Cavendish Laboratory, primitive as it was, was probably the best in England. Not only had J. J. Thomson himself already carried out notable experiments, especially those concerned with the discharge through gases to which reference has just been made, but H. L. Callendar had conducted research on the influence of temperature on the electrical resistance of metals which led to his famous platinum resistance thermometer, destined to play so valuable a part in the measurement of temperature. Incidentally, Callendar went out to Montreal in 1893 to be professor of physics at McGill University, where Rutherford was to succeed him in 1898. However, the work which made the Cavendish Laboratory world famous was about to begin when Rutherford arrived.

On September 24, 1895, J. J. Thomson, who was always known among physicists as "J.J." and will often be so referred to here, wrote to Rutherford, then in London, welcoming him to the laboratory and suggesting that he should become a member of the university. A university regulation had just come into force by which graduates of other universities could be admitted to Cambridge as "Research Students," a new category. Research students could obtain a Cambridge B.A. degree after two years, on the production of a satisfactory thesis containing an account of their research. J. J. Thomson himself said that this regulation made the year 1895 one of the most important in the history of the laboratory. He also records, correctly, that students from other universities were surprised and at first irritated by the restrictions put upon them by the college regulations and particularly by the one which obliged them to be in their rooms before a certain time. In this connection I recollect the case of S. E. Sheppard, famous for his work on the science of the photographic emulsion, who when he came to Cambridge in 1911 as a "research student" already held the degree of Doctor of Science (Docteur ès Sciences) of the Sorbonne, the University of Paris, founded in 1252 and recognized throughout the world as a foremost center of learning. He was obliged to ask the permission of a completely undistinguished man if he wanted to be out after ten-thirty at night. After a year he went to the Eastman Kodak research laboratory at Rochester, where he carried out work of fundamental importance.

The Cavendish Laboratory under J. J. Thomson attracted a large number of research students from other universities: of the workers there in the period 1895 to 1898 less than half had entered the University of Cambridge as undergraduates. The first non-British student to enter the Cavendish Laboratory under the new regulations was a Frenchman, P. Langevin, who later became famous for outstanding researches on, among other things, the theory of magnetism.

A photograph of J. J. Thomson much as he appeared at the time of Rutherford's arrival, although it was actually taken in 1900, is shown in Plate IV. The apparatus is of the kind with which Rutherford worked as a research student in Cambridge. Reference has already been made, in Chapter I, to the Ruhmkorff coil, so prominent on the right. The tube at which the professor is looking is a typical discharge tube of the period. Just above the hand on the switch of the induction coil is an X-ray tube of the kind then in use, to which reference will soon be made. The electromagnet on the left is also characteristic of the physics laboratory of those days.

MORE RESEARCH ON ELECTROMAGNETIC WAVES

Rutherford was actually the first research student to take advantage of the new regulations, though he was only a few minutes ahead of J. S. Townsend. He started by continuing his New Zealand work on detecting electromagnetic waves by the demagnetization of highly magnetized steel needles, these needles being surrounded by a winding which carried the oscillating current produced by the waves acting upon an aerial. The change of magnetization was shown by the change in the deflection of a small suspended magnet placed close to the needles: the movements of this magnet were detected by means of a small mirror attached to it, at which a beam of light from an oil lamp was reflected. Oil lamps were generally used for such purposes in laboratories in those days. In a short time he had observed, with a detector in his friend Townsend's lodgings, electromagnetic waves, six or seven meters in length, generated by an oscillator at the top of the Cavendish Laboratory. The distance traveled by the waves was about half a mile. A little later he detected at the Cavendish signals from the University Observatory, about two miles away.

This was easily a record for distance at the time, which was well before the date of Marconi's inventions. In June 1896 his paper "A Magnetic Detector of Electrical Waves and Some of Its Applications" was communicated to the Royal Society. It gave an account of much of the New Zealand work as well as of the new Cambridge results and appeared in the *Philosophical Transactions of the Royal Society* in the following year. At the time of the communication Rutherford wrote to his mother, "I am in hopes my paper will be published in full in the Philosophical Transactions. This only happens to the best of papers every year and I hope mine will be one of them." He also showed his detector at the annual meeting of the British Association for the Advancement of Science in the autumn of 1896. He was getting about.

Röntgen and the Discovery of X-rays

The year 1895, however, was distinguished by an event which may well be considered as the starting point of modern physics. It was to have a great influence on Rutherford's work: in fact, many years later he said of it that it "marks the beginning of a new and fruitful epoch in physical science in which discoveries of fundamental importance have followed one another in almost unbroken sequence." For on November 8, 1895, Wilhelm Conrad Röntgen, working at Würzburg, discovered X-rays.

The discovery was a consequence of the great interest which had grown up in the discharge of electricity in tubes containing a gas at low pressure. Work in this field was stimulated by the great improvements which, beginning with the work of Heinrich Geissler, about 1855, had been made in the mercury vacuum pump. Inside the tubes used for the discharge were two metallic pieces connected to fine rods or wires passing through the wall, to which the necessary high voltage could be applied. The one that acted as the negative pole was known as the cathode; the other, the positive one, as the anode. The words are derived from the Greek *ana,* up, and *cata,* down, added to *hodos,* way. The electricity is considered as going from the positive pole down to the negative pole.[1]

As the air is pumped out, a stage is reached at which

[1] The terms *anode* and *cathode* were first used by Faraday, who considered what direction of a current round the equator would give the magnetic poles of the earth. "Up" and "down" refer to the rising and setting of the sun along this assumed current path. See Faraday's *Researches,* Series VII, Article 663, January 1834.

a difference of potential of some ten thousands of volts leads to a thick, furry-looking spark. Still further exhaustion, to about a ten-thousandth of atmospheric pressure, leads to a bright green glow, or fluorescence, of the glass, which is due to something streaming from the cathode, as can be shown by introducing suitable obstacles in the way. At certain pressures the path of the cathode beam, or cathode rays, can be seen as a faint, misty glow. Later on more will be said of these cathode rays, which led to fundamental discoveries. William Crookes, who discovered the element thallium, was very active in the investigation of the discharge in evacuated tubes, and sealed-off tubes of certain types that showed the cathode ray discharge were known as Crookes tubes. Philipp Lenard, working with a "window" of extremely thin aluminum foil opposite the cathode, had shown that the cathode rays could pass through this foil and travel a short distance in the air. Other great investigators were also working on the strange phenomena shown by these discharge tubes.

Röntgen was working with discharge tubes covered, for a certain reason, with black paper. He noticed that in a darkened room a screen of fluorescent material, actually barium platinocyanide, lying near the tube glowed brightly when the discharge was passing. He found that the effect took place even when the screen was some feet from the tube. He used both a Crookes tube and a Lenard tube with the same result. He demonstrated the chief properties of the new rays: that they passed through opaque substances, including wood, metals and flesh; that they came from the place where the cathode beam struck the wall of the tube, producing a bright luminescence; that they acted on a photographic plate; that they could discharge electrified bodies by their effect on the air. He at once realized the impor-

tance of the rays for surgery and published a photograph
of the bones of the hand in his first paper.

As a matter of curiosity, Frederick Smith, a physicist
working at Oxford with a Crookes discharge tube, of
the type used by Röntgen, had already observed that
photographic plates kept in a box near the tube were
liable to become fogged, which we now know was a
result of X-rays generated by the tube, but he merely
told his assistant to keep the plates somewhere else.
The fogging of plates was not the subject of his research
and he was not interested in it!

Röntgen published an account of his discoveries,
some days after they were made, in the *Sitzungsberichte*
(Proceedings) of the local scientific society, under the
title "Über eine neue Art von Strahlen" (On a new kind
of rays). Copies of the paper reached England early in
1896, which was the year in which the discovery became generally known, and a translation appeared in
the English scientific journal *Nature* on January 23,
1896. Needless to say, the discovery created a sensation
not only in scientific circles but in the popular press.
To see the bones of the living hand and to be able to
discover needles, splinters, and bullets which had penetrated the flesh struck the popular imagination. I was a
little boy at the time, who had been assured that God
would see him wherever he was but who had had secret
doubts as to whether he could be seen in a cellar or
other windowless room, and I remember thinking that
if there were rays that could penetrate opaque substances it might be true.

Naturally enough, the medical profession hastened to
make use of the new rays, but that does not concern us
here. However, it recalls a true story which will illustrate
Röntgen's character and methods. He discovered X-rays
when he was fifty, and all through his years of patient

research on other subjects he was always seeking fresh controls, always guarding himself against uncertain hypotheses and holding fast to experimental fact. In 1896, just after his sensational discovery, a well-known English medical man, Sir James Mackenzie Davidson, who was a pioneer in the localization of foreign bodies in the human frame by means of X-rays, visited Röntgen. The great man had been describing how he had seen the barium platinocyanide screen shining when the tube was switched on. Sir James asked him, "What did you think?", to which he replied very simply, "I did not think, I investigated." I take it that Röntgen did not mean to suggest that, in making discoveries, one does not have to think, but rather that a few well-directed experiments are worth a deal of unsupported speculation.

In the same year, 1896, the discovery of radioactivity was announced by Henri Becquerel, who found that rays capable of penetrating black paper were spontaneously given out by uranium salts, rays which not only affected the photographic plate but discharged electrified bodies. More is said of this discovery later. The experiments on the discharge of electricity through cathode ray tubes that were to lead to the establishment of the existence of the electron next year were well on their way at Cambridge. Those were exciting times.

COLLABORATION WITH J. J. THOMSON

It is little wonder, then, that Rutherford, with his remarkable sense of what was fundamental in physics, decided to drop his work on detecting Hertzian waves, which did not seem likely to reveal anything basically new, and turned to effects produced by the wonderful new rays, in the investigation of which he was invited to collaborate by J.J.

The subject selected was the effect of X-rays in producing the conduction of electricity in gases. As he said in a letter to Mary Newton, dated April 24, 1896, "I am working with the Professor this term on Röntgen rays. I am a little full up of my old subject and am glad of a change. I expect it will be a good thing for me to work with the Professor for a time. I have done one research to show I can work by myself." He had become engaged to Mary Newton before leaving New Zealand and was to marry her in 1900, when he was settled in Canada. He wrote to her regularly from England, and luckily she preserved all his letters, many of which have been printed. From them we learn several details of his life at the time, for instance of his playing golf with J. J. Thomson, of which he says that he learned to knock the ball a considerable distance, if not very straight, adding, "I don't think, however, I am quite old enough for golf yet." He was then twenty-four. Another illuminating extract from a letter of 1896 is, "Breakfast with McTaggart, Hegelian Philosopher and Fellow of Trinity, but he gave me a very poor breakfast worse luck. His philosophy doesn't count for much when brought face to face with two kidneys, a thing I abhor"—typical Rutherford in sentiment and phrasing. M'Taggart, as he spelled himself, five years older than Rutherford and already well known as a philosopher, had published his first book, *Studies in the Hegelian Dialectic,* at about the time of the breakfast in question, but that did not impress Rutherford, who had quite likely never heard of Hegel and was certainly not interested in him.

Rutherford also wrote many letters to his mother at about this time and, since we are concerned with his incipient work on X-rays, let us hear what he had to

tell her about it. "I have been working pretty steadily
with Professor J. J. Thomson on the X-rays and found
it pretty interesting. Everett, who is the professor's assistant, makes the bulbs which give out the X-rays. You
know one can see the bones of the hand and arm, and
coins inside[2] with the naked eye.

"The method is very simple. A little bulb is exhausted
of air and an electrical discharge sent through. The bulb
then lights up and looks of a greenish colour. The X-rays
are given off and if a piece of cardboard, with a certain
chemical on it, is held near it, metal objects placed behind can be seen through several inches of wood. The
bones of the hand can be clearly seen and if we look at
a spectacle box, no trace of the wood is seen but only
the metal rim and the glass. Aluminium allows the rays
to go through easily. . . . I am not working at that side
of the subject but at some of the actions of X-rays on
substances, etc." The "certain chemical" may have been
phosphorescent zinc sulphide, that is, zinc sulphide with
a trace of a foreign metal that gives it the property of
phosphorescence. It lights up a bright green when exposed to light or to X-rays, and was much used. It may
have been barium platinocyanide, as used by Röntgen,
which is also very effective.

X-RAYS AND THE IONIZATION OF GASES

The work with J. J. Thomson was on what is now
called the ionization of gases effected by X-rays, that is,
the production of positively and negatively charged carriers of electricity, called ions, from the molecules of the
gas. An ionized gas is necessarily a conductor of electricity, since under the influence of an electric field, between parallel metal plates at different voltages, say, the

[2] He probably meant to write "inside a box."

positive carriers will move to the negative plate, or
cathode, and the negative carriers to the positive plate,
or anode, giving up their charges to the plates. About
ten years earlier Svante August Arrhenius, who died in
1927, had put forward this method of conduction by
ions to explain the passage of electricity through solutions of metallic salts, so that it was a familiar notion,
but in the case of a dissolved salt, say sodium chloride,
ions of sodium and chlorine form spontaneously without any radiation or other outside influence.

J. J. Thomson and Rutherford, then, set about investigating the electrical effect of X-rays on gases for
"of all the methods by which we can put a gas into a
state in which it can receive a charge of electricity, none
is more remarkable than that of the Röntgen rays." J. J.
Thomson wrote these words in an account of four lectures given by him at Princeton University in 1896,
the year in which appeared the paper describing the
work with Rutherford which is now in question.[3]

The X-ray tube used in the experiments was a small
bulb, about two and a half inches across, with a con-
cave cathode and an anode consisting of a flat plate set
obliquely, so as to receive the focused cathode rays, as
shown in Plate III. It was, of course, exhausted and
sealed off. The discharge was produced by an induction
coil of the Ruhmkorff type to which reference has already been made. Running these primitive tubes was not
quite the simple matter it might appear to be. To carry
the discharge the gas in the tube must be at a low pressure, but not too low, for if there are too few molecules
of gas present there are too few carriers and the discharge ceases to pass. The pressure may be initially just
right, but under the influence of the discharge the gas

[3] The book founded on these lectures is called *The Discharge
of Electricity through Gases* and was published in 1898.

gradually becomes absorbed by the walls of the tubes, until finally there is not enough of it and the tube ceases to work. Heating the walls of the tube releases some of the gas and so puts things in order again, but all this means that constant expert attention was required for a satisfactory production of rays. To measure the increase or decrease of charge a quadrant electrometer, mentioned in Chapter I, was used, and this was a very tricky instrument. As J.J. himself wrote toward the end of his life, "Another instrument which was exasperating to work with was the old quadrant electrometer. This not infrequently refused to hold its charge, and neither prayers nor imprecations would induce it to do so." The younger Lord Rayleigh, writing of electrometers of this period, says, "J.J. himself used what was called the Elliott pattern, after the name of the inventor. I do not know who designed it, but (to plagiarise Oliver Heaviside in another connection) I suspect that it was primarily the Devil." Good hands, good luck, and a good experimental sense as well as a good head were necessary to work with this primitive apparatus.

To examine the electrical properties of a gas—air in the first case—through which X-rays had passed, J. J. Thomson and Rutherford carried out some simple but fundamental experiments. The X-rays were allowed to pass through an aluminium box to which was attached a long metal tube, at the far end of which was an insulated wire arranged axially along the tube. This wire was connected to the quadrant electrometer, which remained charged as long as the air was still. With a pair of bellows (bellows were a common household article in England at that time, used for helping coal fires to burn merrily) they blew the air exposed to the X-rays along the tube and showed that it discharged the electroscope, and so must retain some of its conducting power for the second or so that it took to travel. If on its way to the testing place the gas was made to pass through a strong electric field it lost its power of discharging the electroscope, since the carriers of electricity were drawn across and removed. J.J. and Rutherford also showed that the gas made conducting by constant exposure to X-rays did not obey Ohm's law, as does a metallic conductor, that is, that the current was not proportional to the potential difference. Rather, as the potential was steadily increased, the current, measured by the rate of change of the charge on the electrometer, did not increase beyond a certain figure, but reached a limiting value—a saturation value, as it was called.

All this and other observations were explained by a simple theory, almost certainly due to J.J., although it appeared, in the paper describing the work carried out with Rutherford, under their joint names. According to this theory, X-rays passing through the gas produced the positively and negatively charged molecules, called ions, which, being of opposite sign, tended to recombine. The rate of recombination was proportional to the square of the number of particles, since the number hitting and the number hit are both involved. Hence the ionized gas, left to itself, would have a conducting power due to the presence of the ions but would gradually lose this conducting power owing to the recombination of the ions. Such behavior would account for the conductivity retained by the air, but diminishing as time went on. Clearly the current through the gas could never attain a value greater than that corresponding to the removal of all the ions as fast as they were produced, which accounts for the saturation effect. This simple theory, mathematically expressed, became the basis of much subsequent work, of great importance, on the electrical behavior of ionized gases.

The paper by J.J. and Rutherford holds a very significant place in the history of modern physics. It laid the foundations of precise and mathematically expressible work on the conduction of electricity in gases, as distinct from general descriptive work. It duly appeared, under the title "On the Passage of Electricity through Gases Exposed to Röntgen Rays," in the *Philosophical Magazine* for November 1896. The *Philosophical Magazine,* which was long the chief journal in which British papers on physical research were published, first appeared in 1789, when what we now call physics was known as natural philosophy, whence the name. Reference has already been made to the *Philosophical Transactions of the Royal Society*. Isaac Newton's epoch-making book appeared in 1687 under the title *Philosophiae Naturalis Principia Mathematica*—The Mathematical Principles of Natural Philosophy—and the term still survives in Scotland, the professor of physics being known as the professor of natural philosophy in many universities there, for instance in Edinburgh. The paper was also presented at the meeting of the British Association for the Advancement of Science held at Liverpool.

It is recorded by Lord Rayleigh that J.J. had sensed Rutherford's value immediately, which his selection to take part in this fundamental investigation seems to confirm. At any rate, there is no doubt that this association in research won for Rutherford a very high place in J.J.'s estimation.

After this work in collaboration with his professor, which brought his name into prominence, Rutherford continued by himself the investigation of the electrical behavior of gases and vapors exposed to Röntgen rays. He extended some of the joint observations and went on to study the absorption of the rays in different gases, proving that those which when irradiated were good conductors of electricity were good absorbers of the radiation. This observation was of importance at the time, showing that energy of the rays was used up in producing ions. It was the subject of a note by J.J., printed at the end of the paper describing the work, on certain implications of the results.

Rutherford then went on to investigate the other properties of the ions produced by the X-rays, in particular their velocity in a unit electric field, now called the mobility, and their rate of recombination, both with various simple gases. In particular, he carefully verified that the rate of recombination was proportional to the square of the number of ions in unit volume. This was the first systematic investigation of ionic mobilities in a gas. The work is typical Rutherford—a search for a simple theory, expressing processes that can easily be pictured and accounting for precise physical measurements.

Both papers describing the work on ionization produced by X-rays were published in 1897 in the *Philosophical Magazine,* the first in April and the second in November. At the end of that year Rutherford was awarded the Coutts Trotter Studentship of £250 a year —"think of it—nearly enough to get married on," as Rutherford wrote to Mary Newton on December 12, 1897. He added, "The best part of the matter is that I can still get the rest of my 1851 Scholarship money, so that I will be quite rich for the time." Naturally enough, Rutherford was always interested in money matters, particularly in those early days.

THE DISCHARGE OF ELECTRICITY BY
ULTRAVIOLET LIGHT

The next subject that Rutherford turned to was the discharge of electricity by ultraviolet light. Beyond the violet end of the visible spectrum are invisible rays, of shorter wave lengths than the violet, which can be detected by, for instance, their action on phosphorescent substances, which they cause to light up, or on a photographic plate. This class of radiation is known as ultraviolet light, or simply the ultraviolet. These rays are very active electrically and chemically: a certain range of them is responsible for sunburn. In 1887 Hertz had discovered that such light, falling on the metal balls of a spark gap, made the spark pass more easily. In the following year Wilhelm Hallwachs had shown that negatively charged metal plates lost their charge when the light fell on them, while positively charged plates did not. After that many others, among whom Julius Elster and Hans F. Geitel[4] were outstanding, had investigated the effect of ultraviolet light in discharging metal bodies standing in air, it being found that different metals lost their charge at different rates in like circumstances. It was, however, not known at the time of Rutherford's work, the account of which was published in 1898, that the action of the light was to cause the ejection of electrons from the metal surface, the phenomenon known under the name of the photoelectric

[4] Elster and Geitel were two well-known German physicists who did all their work, which was excellent, in collaboration, the names always occurring together. In their time, according to a story current in Germany, there was a man who much resembled Geitel in appearance. A stranger, meeting him, said, "Good morning, Herr Elster," to which he replied, "Firstly I am not Elster, but Geitel, and secondly I am not Geitel."

effect, without which there would be no television, for television depends upon this conversion of light effects into electrical effects. Although ultraviolet light is particularly effective, all visible light has a similar effect on appropriate substances. It was at the end of 1899 that J. J. Thomson and Philipp Lenard showed independently, with the irradiated metal in a high vacuum, that the negative charge that left the metal was in the form of particles which had the same mass and charge as the cathode ray particles, that is, were electrons.

Rutherford, like all previous workers, experimented with his metal plates in air at ordinary pressure, and measured the properties of the negatively charged carriers produced, in particular their mobility in an electric field. This he did in the first place by the use of a current of air passing between the surfaces of two parallel plates, one a fine wire gauze to allow the light to pass through it and the other the metal plate on which the ultraviolet light fell. This air current took with it the charged particles and so diminished the current between the plates: the faster the air stream the smaller the current. It is easy to see how such an arrangement would allow the velocity of the carriers in the transverse electrical field to be estimated. Later he used an ingenious method in which he applied an alternating voltage to one of the plates. The distance that the carriers moved out under the influence of the electric field in one direction before they moved back under the reversed field clearly depended upon their velocity and this could be measured by adjusting the distance between the plates. The chief finding was that the mobility of the negatively charged carriers produced by the ultraviolet light was the same whatever the illuminated metal and that it agreed with the mobility of the negative ions produced by X-rays. Rutherford was, of course, deal-

ing with gas molecules which had picked up the electrons emitted from the plate and so with exactly the
same kind of negative carriers as were produced by the
X-rays, but he did not know that. The experiments,
seen from a distance, have, perhaps, no great importance, but they show a most ingenious and fertile experimenter.

BECQUEREL'S DISCOVERY OF
URANIUM RADIATION

In the paper describing this work, which was published in the *Proceedings of the Cambridge Philosophical
Society,* another example of the old use of the word
philosophy, Rutherford refers in passing to the ionization produced by uranium radiation, a first glance at the
subject which in a few years was to make him world-
famous. It has already been mentioned that in 1896 the
great French physicist Henri Becquerel had discovered
that uranium emitted rays which, like X-rays, possessed
the property of discharging electrified bodies standing
in air. The way in which he came to make the discovery
is curious. The X-rays, as discovered by Röntgen, were
given out by the glass of the tube where the rays from
the cathode struck it and were accompanied by a glow
of the glass wall that resembled phosphorescence, which
is the property that some bodies have, after being exposed to a bright light, of themselves giving out light.[5]
Becquerel had been working on the phenomenon of

---

[5] Alarm clocks often have the figures marked with a phosphorescent material, which is kept feebly glowing by a small
amount of radioactive material mixed with it, but it is easy to
show that brief exposure to bright light, say that of a hand
torch in a dark room, makes them come to a brighter glow,
which gradually decays. This is phosphorescence.

phosphorescence and, as soon as Röntgen's discovery was made known, it occurred to him that possibly the new rays were connected with the phosphorescence and that phosphorescent substances in general gave out such rays. Certain compounds of uranium with which he was very familiar exhibit a strong phosphorescence and he decided to try out the matter with those compounds.

Accordingly he placed such substances on a photographic plate wrapped in black paper and duly found that after a time the photographic plate was affected, just as it would have been by X-rays. However, he soon discovered that the effect had nothing to do with the phosphorescence, since it took place equally well if the uranium salts had not recently been exposed to light and so were not phosphorescing. He then found that it was the uranium alone that was the cause of the image on the photographic plate, whether it was in the form of a phosphorescent salt or not—any uranium compound would produce it. He also found that the rays which the uranium gave out resembled X-rays in that they would pass through considerable thicknesses of metal and other opaque substances and would discharge an electroscope.

It seems natural that this should have intrigued Rutherford, who had done so much work on the ionization produced by X-rays. Accordingly, after completing his work on the electrical effects of ultraviolet light, he began to investigate the effects produced by the rays from uranium, with the object of seeing how far the two types of radiation resembled one another.

ALPHA AND BETA RADIATION

It had been found that X-rays were complex, that is, that they comprised radiations with different powers of penetrating solid bodies, and Rutherford set about measuring the power of penetration of the uranium radiations, using the ionization produced as a measure of the intensity of the rays. He used two large horizontal parallel plates, with a difference of potential between them, on the lower of which he placed a layer of uranium compound and this he covered with very thin metal foils, measuring with an electrometer the ionization produced with various numbers of foils. He found that—but let us use his own words, simple and direct as usual. "These experiments show that the uranium radiation is complex, and that there are present at least two distinct types of radiation—one that is very readily absorbed, which will be termed for convenience the α radiation, and the other of a more penetrating character, which will be termed the β radiation." Alpha (α) and beta (β) are the first two letters of the Greek alphabet. He showed that the penetrating power of the beta radiations was of the same order as that of X-rays emitted from the average bulb, whereas that of the alpha rays was vastly less, only a small proportion of them penetrating an aluminium sheet a thousandth of an inch in thickness, according to these early experiments. It was left for Rutherford to show later that the alpha and the beta radiations were of quite a different nature, the alpha rays consisting of charged atoms of the gas helium, and the beta rays being a stream of rapid electrons, both shot out spontaneously. The alpha particles were later Rutherford's pet—and how he made them work! In this first paper, however, he could only conclude, because of their power of ionizing gases, that the two types of radiation from uranium were similar, respectively, to Röntgen rays and to the secondary radiation—which we now know to be electrons—emitted by metals when Röntgen rays fall on them. "The cause and origin of the radiations continuously emitted by uranium is a mystery"—but it was a mystery that Rutherford was later to clear up.

J. J. THOMSON AND THE DISCOVERY
OF THE ELECTRON

While Rutherford was engaged in his work on the ionization produced by X-rays, J.J. was carrying out a research on cathode rays which led to the discovery of the electron. This discovery had so profound an influence on the course of the physics of the time, including Rutherford's work, that something must be said of it.

The way in which, at a certain range of low pressure, cathode rays appear in the discharge tube has been described in connection with Röntgen's discovery. Crookes had shown that the path of the beam was turned aside by a magnet and that the direction of the deflection was that to be expected if the rays were negatively charged particles speeding from the cathode. A beam of charged particles is equivalent to an electric current whose strength is proportional to the speed and to the size of the traveling charge. Jean Perrin, a great Frenchman who was to receive the Nobel Prize in 1926 for fundamental work on molecular behavior, had shown by a direct experiment that the rays carried a negative charge. It had also been shown that the cathode rays were deflected in an electric field in the direction to be expected if they carried a negative charge. In spite of these discoveries the nature of the cathode rays was a subject of doubt: while some thought that they consisted of a stream of small particles of some kind, others conjectured that they were something in the nature of a wave propagation. It was left for J.J. to show that they were a stream of particles of a hitherto unimagined kind.

He measured the deflection of a narrow beam of cathode rays, in both a magnetic and an electric field. As this method was afterward used by Rutherford to establish the nature of the α rays, it may be well to explain briefly how it works. An electric field exerts a force on a charged particle which depends upon the size of the charge only, and is the same whether it is moving or is at rest. The acceleration caused by the electric force, however, depends upon the mass, so that the deflection, the moving aside, of a flying charged particle, will depend on the ratio of the charge to the mass, and, of course, on the time for which the force acts.

A magnetic field has no action on a charged particle at rest. A moving charged particle is, however, equivalent to an electric current: the faster the particle the larger the corresponding current. A wire conveying an electric current in a magnetic field tends to move sideways, at right angles to itself and to the field. The movement of a beam of charged particles, then, in a magnetic field will depend upon the velocity as well as upon the ratio of charge to mass. Of course in both an electric and a magnetic field the sideways movement of the beam in a given length of path will depend upon the velocity, since that governs the time for which the particles are exposed to the field, but this consideration is the same in both cases, while the velocity has an independent effect in the case of the magnetic field.

The upshot of all this is that by measuring the deflection of the beam in an electric and in a magnetic field both the ratio of the charge to the mass of the particles which make up the beam, and the velocity of the particles, can be found. Needless to say, there are experi-

mental difficulties, such as securing the right pressure
in the exhausted tube, but these difficulties J. J. Thomson overcame. He found that the ratio of charge to mass,
usually written *e/m*, was the same whatever the nature
of the gas in the tube or of the metal of the electrode
and that it was 770 times greater than it is for a charged
hydrogen ion in the electrolysis of a liquid.[6] This finding could only mean that the charge was much greater
or the mass much smaller in the case of the cathode
particles than in the case of the hydrogen ion—and the
hydrogen atom is the lightest atom known. J.J., who
called these particles "corpuscles," inclined to the view
that they were, in fact, very much smaller and lighter
than atoms, the charge being the same as that on the
hydrogen ion.

A little later J.J. measured the charge on the electron
by a most ingenious method, involving the condensation of minute water drops on individual electrons, and
found it to be the same as the unit charge on the familiar ions found in solutions of salts. This enabled him to
find the mass of the electron, which, from what has
been said, was, according to his experiments, 1/770 of
that of the hydrogen atom. This was a very rough determination: W. Kaufmann's experiment gave a much
better value. But the great point established was that
matter contained particles of mass very much less than
the lightest atom known, that of hydrogen, corpuscles
which could therefore be regarded as part of the structure of all atoms. As J.J. himself wrote in 1899, "I
regard the atom as containing a large number of smaller
bodies which I will call corpuscles; these corpuscles are
equal to each other; the mass of the corpuscle is the

[6] A little later W. Kaufmann found the more accurate value
of 1840 times. A modern value is 1822.

mass of the negative ion in a gas at low pressure," that is, is the mass of a cathode ray particle.

This was a discovery of the greatest importance, the first subatomic particle. A little later the famous Dutch physicist H. A. Lorentz gave the "corpuscle" the name "electron," which has been used ever since. The name was, as a matter of fact, originally suggested by the Irishman Johnstone Stoney in 1894 for the unit charge on ions in an electrolytic liquid, which, as has been said, is of the same magnitude. The establishment of the existence of the electron was a fresh stage in the new physics which was so rapidly growing up and necessarily had an influence on Rutherford's work.

At the time of its discovery, and for years afterward, the electron seemed to have no interest but a purely scientific one—in fact, a toast at the annual Cavendish Laboratory dinner was, "The electron: may it never be of any use to anybody." What has sprung from the invention of the thermionic valve and later the transistor, which depend for their action on the electron, is familiar to everybody—television, for one thing. But that is another story.

The discovery of the electron was, possibly, the chief event in the Cavendish Laboratory in Rutherford's time there as a young man, but other men destined to become famous were working there with joy and enthusiasm on allied problems. There was C. T. R. Wilson, who showed that gaseous ions, positive or negative, act as centers for the condensation of minute drops of water in clouds produced in laboratory vessels. This striking discovery was used by J.J. to determine the value of the charge on ions produced by Röntgen rays, as already mentioned. In 1911 C. T. R. Wilson himself showed how it could be applied to photograph the paths of moving charged particles in his world-famous cloud

chamber, for which he was later awarded the Nobel
Prize. The operation of this cloud chamber is discussed in Chapter VI. H. A. Wilson, afterward professor of physics at the Rice Institute, Houston, Texas,
was working on the electrical properties of flame gases,
with which J. A. McClelland, afterward professor of
physics at the National University of Ireland, was also
concerned. J. S. Townsend, afterward Wykeham professor of physics at Oxford, was busy with the diffusion
of ions and the electrical properties of newly liberated
gases. There were others doing work of importance. It
was a gallant band.

APPOINTMENT AS PROFESSOR OF
PHYSICS AT McGILL

We left Rutherford completing, in this atmosphere of
delight in discovery, his work on "Uranium Radiation
and the Electrical Conduction Produced by It," as the
paper describing it was entitled. Before this paper was
published, however, he had left the Cavendish. On April
22, 1898, he wrote to Mary Newton that the professorship of physics at McGill University, Montreal, seemed
about to become vacant, but that the salary was only
£500 a year and he would not go in unless J.J. ad-
vised him to. He added, "Personally, next to New Zealand I would rather like Canada, as I believe things
are very jolly over there." He seemed rather in two
minds, but in ten days had decided to apply for the post,
especially as he thought his chance of getting a Trinity
College Fellowship, which would have maintained him
in comfort for some time, very small. "I know perfectly
well that if I had gone through the regular Cambridge
course and done a third of the work I have done, I
would have got a Fellowship bang off," which is proba-

bly true. In the course of time, however—that is, twenty-one years later—when he succeeded J. J. Thomson as Cavendish professor, he was made a Fellow of Trinity College.[7]

Two months after the letter just quoted he was writing that he would probably be appointed to the McGill chair and that great things would be anticipated of him—"I am expected to do a lot of original work and to form a research school in order to knock the shine out of the Yankees!" He also discussed finances, in which he was always interested, and said that they ought, when married, to do very comfortably on £400 a year and put the rest aside. On August 3, 1898, he wrote a joyful letter saying that he had been appointed and that matrimony was looming in the distance. To put us once more in touch with finance at the time, a first-class passage to Canada then cost £12. He left England on September 8, 1898. He was twenty-seven years old.

It may be well to conclude this account of his young days in Cambridge with words from J.J.'s testimonial, which no doubt played a major part in securing the post for him: "I have never had a student with more enthusiasm or ability for original research than Mr. Rutherford and I am sure that if elected he would establish a distinguished school of Physics at Montreal." Like Bickerton's prediction on his departure from New Zealand, this was to be duly fulfilled.

[7] At Oxford and Cambridge the colleges which make up the university are accustomed to elect certain graduates who have particularly distinguished themselves to the position of Fellow. The Fellow of a college has granted to him pleasant apartments in the college and receives an income adequate, especially in Rutherford's time, for an agreeable life.

Chapter IV

THE McGILL LABORATORY, MONTREAL

In his nine years at McGill University, 1898 to 1907, Rutherford's researches and those of the collaborators whom he gathered round him were entirely devoted to radioactivity, the subject with which his name is inseparably connected. The fundamental nature of this work, which had so profound an influence on the conception of atomic nature and processes, was acknowledged by the award of the Nobel Prize in 1908 "for his investigation into the disintegration of the elements and the chemistry of radioactive substances," the word *chemistry* being no doubt introduced because the prize was that for chemistry and not for physics! The prize for physics went to Gabriel Lippman, a pioneer in color photography, and presumably the awarders felt that it was time that Rutherford received a Nobel Prize and that the behavior of the radioactive elements might be considered as a branch of chemistry.

PIERRE AND MARIE CURIE

Since we shall be dealing so much with radioactivity, it may be well to review briefly the state of knowledge of the subject at the end of the century. How, in 1896, Henri Becquerel discovered that uranium spontaneously gave out rays which affected the photographic plate and rendered air a conductor of electricity has already been described. Now enter upon the scene the two Curies, husband and wife, who took up the subject of this mysterious activity—for the fact that uranium, without being in any way excited, continued steadily to emit penetrating rays no matter how it was chemically combined was most mysterious. Pierre Curie, born in Paris in 1859, was already well known as a physicist, having with his brother discovered what is known as "piezoelectricity"[1] and further having done important work on magnetism which led to the discovery of what is known as the Curie effect. He was killed in a street accident in 1906.

Madame Curie was born in 1867, as Manya Sklodowska, in Warsaw, Poland, at that time under oppressive Russian government. She longed to study in Paris and in 1891 she traveled thither by railway in great hardship, fourth class, for she was exceedingly short of money. Fourth-class railway carriages in Germany were like luggage vans, with a few benches in them. She studied physics and chemistry at the Sorbonne, the University of Paris, and in 1895 married Pierre Curie. She took the French name Marie, by which she is always known, in place of the Polish Manya, and retained her maiden name, appearing as Marie Sklodowska Curie. Her first research was on the magnetic properties of steels, magnetism having been, as mentioned, a subject in which her husband had achieved outstanding results. They lived in poverty, but they were both animated by an overwhelming enthusiasm for scientific research and appear to have cared little for what would ordinarily be

[1] The name given to the phenomenon, shown by certain crystals, of developing electric charges on particular faces when subjected to pressure in certain directions.

considered comfort or for such refinements as conventional clothing.

Inspired by the researches of Becquerel, Marie Curie took up work on the rays emitted by uranium in a variety of compounds and showed that the amount of activity depended only upon the amount of uranium present. She also studied compounds of thorium: uranium was the element of highest atomic weight then known and thorium came next to it. She found that the thorium salts and minerals sent out strong radiations similar to those from uranium. The method which she used was very simple: two horizontal metal plates, a layer of the powdered substance being sprinkled on the lower one, with a difference of potential of 100 volts between them and an electroscope with which to measure the passage of electric charge. C. G. Schmidt in Germany independently discovered the activity of thorium at the same time. So now, in 1898, there were two different elements known to send out spontaneously and steadily radiations that rendered air conducting, in a way that J. J. Thomson and Rutherford had shown to be due to the formation of charged molecules, called ions.

After the discovery of the spontaneous emission of rays by thorium Mme. Curie made a systematic search for active matter with a large number of minerals containing uranium and thorium. Among the substances tested was pitchblende, a variety of uranium compound so called on account of the black pitch-like luster of a freshly broken surface. Surprisingly, some specimens of this mineral showed many times the activity to be expected from the amount of uranium in them. Hence Mme. Curie concluded that the pitchblende must contain, besides uranium, small quantities of some much more active substance which had never been detected—a simple but by no means obvious conclusion.

THE DISCOVERY OF RADIUM

She and her husband therefore set about trying to isolate this substance by separating chemically all the many elements contained in the mineral, and testing them in their usual way, with parallel plates and an electrometer, to see how far they produced ions in the air. It was in their first paper on these tests that the word *radio-actif* (or *radio-active,* according to gender) was used for the first time and in the next paper that *radio-activité* was first used, translated as "radioactivity" in the scientific weekly *Nature* for November 16, 1898, the first appearance of the word in English.

As a result of these researches it was found that the samples of bismuth and of barium separated out from the pitchblende were highly radioactive. As neither ordinary bismuth nor ordinary barium shows any activity, this could only mean that very radioactive unknown elements, behaving chemically like bismuth and barium respectively, were present in the pitchblende. Mme. Curie named the one associated with bismuth *polonium,* in honor of her native land (it was later to be known as radium F), while that associated with barium was called *radium.*

The experiments that led to the discovery of radium were carried out under primitive conditions in an abandoned shed that nobody wanted. The material used was a ton of uranium residue from pitchblende from the State Manufactory at Joachimstal, luckily presented by the Austrian government, for the Curies could not have afforded to pay for it and had no research funds. The reasoning that led to the discovery was quite simple: the activity of uranium compounds had been shown in a general way to depend only upon, and to be proportional to, the amount of uranium present; the activity of pitchblende was much too high for its uranium content and therefore some highly active substance must be associated with the uranium. The method of investigation was quite simple: the different elements in the pitchblende were separated out by the established methods and their activity was measured by evaporating the filtrates to dryness and testing them for the ionization produced in the elementary way already described. Genius has been defined as the infinite capacity for taking pains, but there is something more to it than that, new fundamental notions. The Curies had both.

Somewhat later, in January 1902, Rutherford wrote to his mother from McGill, "I am now busy writing up papers for publication and doing fresh work. I have to keep going, as there are always people on my track. I have to publish my present work as rapidly as possible in order to keep in the race. The best sprinters in this road of investigation are Becquerel and the Curies in Paris, who have done a great deal of very important work in the subject of radioactive bodies during the past few years." Such was the opinion of the man best able, perhaps, to judge.

After the discovery that a highly active substance, radium, was associated with the barium, the radium was separated out by refined methods, depending upon differences of solubility of salts of the two elements, for radium was shown to be an element. Radium is prodigiously active, for in pitchblende there is only about one part of radium to three million parts of uranium, and yet the activity due to the radium content is several times that of the uranium. It was some years before Mme. Curie separated out enough of the element radium to determine its atomic weight, which takes us well into the period of Rutherford's work at McGill. It may be added that radium is expensive. During the First World War the price rose to £25 per milligram, or, at the exchange rate at the time, more than $3 million an ounce. But then there was not very much of it separated out. It has been estimated that up to 1940 the total world production was a little over two pounds weight.

In 1899 A. Debierne, working with uranium residues for the Curies, discovered a new radioactive element, which he called actinium. Thus before the end of the century three radioactive elements were known, radium, thorium, and actinium, each, as was to appear later, the head of a family of radioactive elements. There was also polonium, which was later to be shown to belong to the radium family. But these are matters that Rutherford and Soddy's work at McGill was to make clear.

We now return to Rutherford's arrival at McGill. McGill College, granted university status by Royal Charter in 1821, was founded as the result of a bequest of James McGill, a merchant and prominent citizen of Montreal, who on his death in 1813 left about £40,-000 for the purpose. In 1898 it had what were for the time very good laboratories. The professor whom Rutherford succeeded was Hugh L. Callendar, who returned to take up a professorship in England. As Rutherford wrote to Mary Newton shortly before leaving Cambridge, "McGill is a very important place to be at, for Callendar was a F.R.S.,[2] and a Fellow of Trinity, and quite a pot in the scientific world, so I will be expected to do great things." The physics laboratory—"the best of its kind in the world," Rutherford commented—was very well supplied with apparatus and generously sup-

[2] F.R.S. means Fellow of the Royal Society, Britain's highest scientific distinction.

ported by a millionaire named Sir William Macdonald, who was a curious character. Although so rich, he lived on £250 a year, so that he thought professors should be comfortable on £500 a year, the stipend that they all received at McGill. Macdonald, a wholesale tobacconist who had made all his money out of tobacco, "cash before delivery," very much disliked smoking, which he considered a filthy habit. A. S. Eve, who worked with Rutherford at McGill and afterward became professor of physics there, tells how one day in 1903 Rutherford rushed into his room breathless, saying, "Open the windows, put away your pipes, hide your tobacco." To the reply, "All right, but what is the trouble?" he rejoined, "Hurry up! Macdonald is coming round the laboratory." Yet it was the smoking of tobacco that enabled Macdonald to equip the laboratory and to furnish such things as a liquid air machine and money for the purchase of radium bromide and other laboratory luxuries, as they were required. Rutherford's title, and that of his successors at McGill, was Macdonald professor of physics.

THE PROPERTIES OF THORIUM EMANATION

Rutherford's first discovery at McGill was of a new class of radioactive substance, with peculiar properties. He found that thorium, besides emitting alpha and beta radiations, gave out an active substance that could be carried from it by a current of air and seemed to be of the nature of a gas, since it passed through cotton wool with the air, which particles of dust would not have done. A little later he showed, with Frederick Soddy, that it could be condensed from the air by extreme cold, but was not affected by a high temperature, which likewise pointed to its being a gas. It also proved to be chemically inactive, that is, it did not combine with other elements, which showed it to belong to the class known as rare or inert gases, of which helium, neon, and argon are well-known members.[3] Such gases consist of single atoms, and not, like most gases, of molecules made up of atoms. Oxygen and hydrogen, for instance, are made up of molecules, each of which contains two similar atoms in combination.

The radioactivity of the thorium emanation, as it was called, was proved by blowing a slow stream of air over thorium into a vessel with an insulated electrode at 100 volts and showing with an electrometer that it caused the leakage of electricity typical of ionized air. As long as the flow of air through the vessel was steady, the leak was steady. If, however, air containing the thorium emanation was shut up in the vessel, a new phenomenon made itself evident. The leak due to the radioactivity became slower and slower as time went on, as if the radioactivity were decreasing. Rutherford showed that this was not due to ions being removed, because if the emanation was merely allowed to stand, without the application of any potential difference, and so without any displacement of charged particles, it lost activity in exactly the same way.

The loss of activity was rapid: it fell to half its observed value at any moment, whatever that might be, in 54 seconds. The matter cannot be better or more simply expressed than in Rutherford's own words. Writing in 1906 of the behavior of the thorium emanation, separated from the thorium, he says, "In the first 54 seconds

[3] The inert gases are generally said not to enter into chemical combination with other elements. Although recently as a chemical feat certain compounds involving them have been prepared, they may certainly be said to be very inert compared to the other elements.

PLATE I. Rutherford, the portrait painted by Oswald Birley in 1932, which hangs in the rooms of the Royal Society. (The Royal Society)

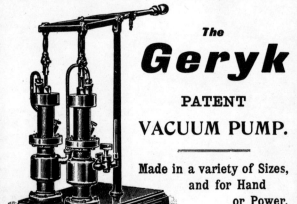
PLATE II. Advertisement of 1897, showing the type of vacuum pump then in use. As there printed, "By its aid Röntgen Tubes can be exhausted."

PLATE III. Advertisement of 1897, showing the type of X-ray tube then in use and referring to the induction coils and batteries needed to make it function.

PLATE IV. J. J. Thomson as he was when Rutherford worked with him, surrounded by apparatus of the period. (The Cavendish Laboratory, Cambridge)

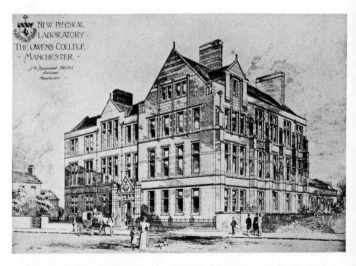

NEW PHYSICAL
LABORATORY ·
THE OWENS COLLEGE.
· MANCHESTER ·
J. W. Beaumont ARIBA
Assistant
Manchester

PLATE V. The laboratory building at Manchester in Rutherford's time, from the architect's drawing.

the activity is reduced to half value; in twice that time, i.e. in 108 seconds, the activity is reduced to one quarter value, and in 162 seconds to one eighth value, and so on. This rate of decay of the activity of the thorium emanation is its characteristic feature, and serves as a definite physical method of distinguishing the thorium emanation from that of radium or of actinium, which decay at very different rates." The emanation which was given off from radium was discovered by Friedrich Ernst Dorn, a distinguished German physicist much concerned with X-rays and radioactivity, just after Rutherford's discovery of the thorium emanation. The actinium emanation was discovered a little later.

It can be shown mathematically that such decrease of activity to a fixed fraction in a given time interval, taken at any stage of the process, will occur if the rate of loss of activity at any moment is proportional to the activity at that moment. Any process where the rate of change at any moment is proportional to the amount of the thing changing which is present at that moment is said to obey an exponential law. The exponential law is so important for radioactive change that it may be well to illustrate it by a simple example.

Suppose water to be flowing slowly out of a tall glass cylinder through a fine horizontal tube at the bottom of the cylinder. The rate of flow through the tube will be proportional to the pressure, that is, will be proportional to the amount of water in the cylinder at the moment considered. This rate of loss will get slower and slower as the level of the water falls, according to exactly the same law as governs the decrease of radioactivity in the case of the thorium emanation and indeed, as will appear later, in the case of all radioactive substances. For instance, if we are told that the time for half the water to flow out is three minutes, then in six minutes there will be one quarter of the water left, in nine minutes one eighth of the water left, and so on.

The characteristic time taken to express the rate of diminution, or rate of decay, as it is called in the radio-active case, is the time to fall to one half, which is called the half value period, or simply the half period or, again, the half life. Thus the half life for thorium emanation is 54 seconds, for radium emanation 3.85 days, and for actinium emanation only 3.9 seconds.

This activity decreasing with time was something essentially new, which turned out to be of prime importance for an understanding of the nature of radioactivity. The activity of thorium and uranium, as far as was known at the time of this discovery, did not change as time went on. We know now that the activity of all radioactive substances decays, but in the case of thorium and uranium the half life, determined by special methods to be indicated later, runs into hundreds of millions of years, so that it is not hard to understand that no change in activity was noticed.

Let us return to Rutherford's work on thorium. He further found that any substance, no matter what its chemical nature, left in contact with the gaseous thorium emanation, became itself radioactive, and he traced this activity to a very thin layer of material which could be dissolved off the surface and then obtained by evaporation of the solution. Although there was far too little of it to be seen, its presence could be detected by its intense radiation. He called it the active deposit of thorium. The deposit was positively charged, for it collected on a negatively charged metal, a wire for instance.

A WIFE FROM NEW ZEALAND

The two papers describing the properties of thorium emanation, and of the deposit formed by it, were completed in 1899 and published early in 1900. About this time Rutherford was making plans to go to New Zealand to marry Mary Newton. On the 31st of December, 1899, the last day of the old year, he wrote to her, "Everyone is much interested to have a look at the strange creature I am going to bring from New Zealand. I am sure you will find a number of friends you will like among the College people, who will do anything they can for you. Professor Owens, the electrical engineering professor, is a great friend of mine.[4] He is taking a flat next year and his chief object in doing so is to prepare for suppers for you and me, etc. In fact he said he designed his quarters especially with that object in view."

In the early summer of 1900 Rutherford duly went to New Zealand by way of San Francisco and the marriage took place. He returned with his wife in September, making an interesting journey by way of Honolulu, Vancouver, and the Canadian Rockies. They settled down in the autumn, according to Eve, in a comfortable little house on an economical scale. The Rutherfords always lived on an economical scale, even in times of prosperity. In March 1901 a daughter was born to them, Eileen Mary, their only child. Twenty years later she was to marry the well-known physicist Ralph Howard Fowler, who died in 1944. She herself died at an early age in 1930.

About the time of the birth of his daughter, Ruther-

[4] Incidentally, Rutherford had published with him a short note on thorium and uranium radiation.

ford was considering whether he should stand for the professorship of physics at Edinburgh, which had become vacant. J. J. Thomson wrote advising him to apply for the chair if he wanted to return to England, but at the same time warning him that he did not think his chances very good, as a local man was up for the post and the election was made by a body of local men who did not know anything of physics. (This kind of situation cannot, of course, arise today—we hope.) He added that he quite appreciated the isolation of scientific workers in the Colonies. In the end Rutherford decided not to apply. He was soon to embark on investigations which made his name known all over the scientific world. He also was about to attract collaborators of remarkable ability, so that any feelings of isolation must have been greatly diminished.

COLLABORATION WITH SODDY

A particularly happy and profitable association was that with Frederick Soddy. Soddy, born on September 2, 1877, and so nearly six years younger than Rutherford, had graduated at Oxford, where he showed a great interest in chemistry. At the age of twenty-three he went to Toronto in search of a professorship. His quest failing, he took, in May 1900, a junior post in the chemistry department at McGill, attracted, it is said, by the excellent laboratory equipment. In September of the same year he met Rutherford, whose first papers on thorium had appeared early in the year, and there ensued a period of collaboration which produced a completely new outlook on radioactivity, involving a revolution in the accepted notions concerning the nature of the atom.

The collaboration was a particularly fortunate one. Rutherford had had no serious training in chemistry, a detailed knowledge of which was essential for the separation of the radioactive elements, but he was, of course, an unrivaled expert in the measurement of radioactivity by ionization methods and in the design and manipulation of apparatus for the purpose. Soddy was an expert chemist, but with no experience of radioactive measurements. Both were enthusiasts for experiment and profoundly interested in atomic conceptions, and, of course, both were men of genius.

The first piece of work carried out by Rutherford and Soddy was on thorium, and showed the effect of the collaboration of a chemist. They found that a very active substance, which they called thorium X, could be separated from thorium by a simple chemical operation. William Crookes had already separated from uranium an active substance called by him uranium X, and accordingly the thorium product was similarly named. The behavior of this thorium X and the thorium which had been freed from it was essentially involved in Rutherford and Soddy's new theory of radioactivity, the importance of which cannot be overrated.

Some account will now be given of this theory, contained in two papers entitled "The Cause and Nature of Radioactivity." As the collaborators said in the introduction to these papers, "Radioactivity is shown to be accompanied by electrical changes in which new types of matter are being continually produced." It must be remembered that the belief current at the time was that no new types of matter had been produced since the creation.

The experimental basis of their new doctrine was the behavior of thorium, which, as has been indicated, had been so carefully investigated by Rutherford, first alone and then in collaboration with Soddy. The major part of the activity of thorium could be removed by chemical processes, in particular by precipitation with ammonia, and was attributed to the substance named thorium X. This substance therefore had chemical properties distinct from those of thorium, but it was present in very small quantities, always associated with considerable residues possessing the same chemical properties. The thorium freed from thorium X recovered its radioactive properties, as established by the radiations emitted, while the separated thorium X lost its radioactivity in the usual exponential manner, the time to half activity being about four days. In four days, likewise, the thorium recovered half its activity.

Rutherford and Soddy showed that this behavior could be simply explained if the thorium recovered its lost activity by forming thorium X at a constant rate, while the thorium X so formed decayed in the exponential way characteristic of radioactive substances. For, starting with thorium freed from thorium X, as the amount of thorium X increases the faster will it decay, the rate of decay being proportional to the quantity present at the moment. In the end this rate of decay will equal the fixed rate of formation, when there will be equilibrium. The water-flow analogy would be a tall vessel, with a small escape tube at the bottom, into which water was slowly flowing at a fixed rate. The level would rise until the pressure at the bottom was such that the water ran out as fast as it ran in, when the level would remain fixed. That the thorium X is formed at a fixed rate is due to the extremely slow decay of the thorium: it does decay, like all other radioactive elements, but the half period runs into thousands of millions of years. The change of rate in a human lifetime is, then, far too small to be perceptible.

The essential theory, then, was that, firstly, thorium X was a distinct type of matter, a distinct element, with definite chemical properties different from those of thorium itself; that radioactivity was an atomic property, since the rate of decay, and the radioactive properties in general, were not in any way affected by chemical combination; that the formation of thorium X at a constant rate could only be explained by the thorium changing into thorium X, so slowly that the quantity of thorium was not noticeably diminished. "Since therefore," they wrote, "radioactivity is at once an atomic phenomenon and accompanied by chemical changes in which new types of matter are produced, these changes must be occurring within the atom, and the radioactive elements must be undergoing spontaneous transformation."

They soon took things further by showing that the "disintegration theory," as it was called, explained other features of the activity associated with thorium. The thorium X was proved to be responsible for the thorium emanation, which in its turn produced the active deposit, radioactive transformation being in question in both cases.

The theory of atomic change was strongly supported by the observation that the radioactive transformations took place at the same rate over a wide range of temperature. The rate of all ordinary chemical changes is very dependent on temperature. Rutherford and Soddy showed that the same fundamental concepts they had used for thorium could be successfully applied to the behavior of radium and radium emanation and of uranium and uranium X.

THE NATURE OF ALPHA AND GAMMA RADIATIONS

Of great concern in the question of radioactive transformations was the nature of the alpha and gamma radiations. In textbooks of physics it is stated without much ado that the alpha radiation consists of particles which are atoms of helium with a positive charge of 2 units,[5] the magnitude of unit charge being that of the charge on the electron, while the gamma radiation is of the same nature as X-rays. However, it took Rutherford and his collaborators many years of hard work to settle this, and, as an indication of the labor that is necessary to determine such apparently simple matters, we may briefly indicate the history of the determination of the nature of the alpha particle.

When the alpha radiation was first discovered by Rutherford it was given a special name on account of the fact that it was so easily absorbed—completely stopped, in fact, by a few inches of air—whereas the beta radiations would go through metal sheets some hundredths of an inch in thickness, and gamma rays were more penetrating still. Early attempts to deflect the alpha rays by a magnetic field were unsuccessful. It was not until 1903, four years after their discovery, that Rutherford, letting the rays pass through a number of narrow parallel slits, succeeded in showing that they were deflected by both an electric and a magnetic field; bending their paths stopped their passage, since when turned aside a little they struck the plates bounding the slits. The direction of the deflection showed that they were positively charged. The velocity, which could be found by the deflection in an electric and in a magnetic field, as explained when J. J. Thomson's experiments on the electron were described, was, for the particles from radium, about a tenth of that of light. Now the ratio of the charge to the mass (e/m) was found to be very roughly one half of what it was for the

[5] This, we now know, means that an alpha particle is a helium nucleus, but the nuclear structure of the atom was not discovered by Rutherford until long after the McGill period.

hydrogen atom, so that if, as was at first supposed, the charge was equal to the charge on the electron, but positive, the mass must be twice that of the hydrogen atom. This is what Rutherford at one time believed to be the case.

What was required, to settle finally the problem of the mass, was, then, to measure the charge on the alpha particle. This, however, proved to be a very difficult task, and was not satisfactorily accomplished until 1908, when Rutherford, working with Geiger at Manchester, with a high vacuum, a magnetic field to turn aside troublesome electrons, and a method of allowing for the effect of the gamma rays, found that the charge was double the electronic charge. This was proof positive that the mass was four times that of the hydrogen atom, that is, was the mass of the helium atom, but before then, in 1904, Rutherford had stated that the alpha particles "in all probability" consisted of helium atoms expelled at the successive stages of the disintegration.

Another line of investigation that had led to the same conclusion depended upon spectroscopy, the investigation of the precise nature of the light sent out by a gas when an electric discharge, or high temperature, makes it luminous. This light consists of rays of several distinct frequencies, or wave lengths, characteristic of the gas in question. The instrument known as the spectroscope spreads the light of different frequencies into a range of different positions, each very narrow region of which corresponds to a different particular frequency; in other words, particular frequencies characteristic of a given luminous gas are represented by bright lines in particular positions, which make up the spectrum of a gas. A single specially bright line, of accurately measured position, may be taken as evidence of the gas to which it belongs. Now in 1868 a bright line had been discovered

by Norman Lockyer in the spectrum of the chromo-
sphere, an outer region of the sun, which did not correspond to any known element. It was put down to an
unknown element supposed to exist only in the sun, and
christened helium, from *helios,* the Greek for sun. In
1895 the famous chemist William Ramsay, investigating
a gas enclosed in cleveite, a mineral rich in uranium,
found that it gave the characteristic spectrum of the
hypothetical solar element. It was earth-born helium,
later recognized to be alpha particles discharged by the
uranium through the ages and trapped in the mineral.
It also exists in natural gas, from which it has been
separated on a commercial scale in America.

In 1903 Soddy returned to England to work with
Ramsay. Together they showed that a gas, very small
in amount, liberated by radium, gave, along with the
lines of familiar gases with which it was mixed, the
strongest and most characteristic line of the helium
spectrum when an electric discharge was passed through
it. This demonstrated that radium gave rise to helium,
but did not definitely prove that the helium was alpha
particles that had lost their speed. Finally in 1908, after
his return to England, Rutherford, in conjunction with
T. Royds, clinched the matter. They enclosed radium
emanation, which gives out swift alpha particles, in a
fine glass tube with a wall so thin—a few ten-thousandths
of an inch in thickness—that alpha particles could pass
through it. The gas which formed, in very small quantities, in an enclosing tube was then compressed by mercury into a very fine tube through which an electric
discharge was passed. A strong spectrum showing all
the characteristic helium lines appeared. But if helium
gas was put in the thin-walled inner tube no such
spectrum was visible, so that the appearance of helium
in the outer tube was not a question of helium diffusing

through the wall of the thin inner tube, but of high speed helium atoms being shot through the tube wall. Alpha particles *were* helium atoms. This clinching proof came ten years after the first discovery by Rutherford of the alpha radiation. It is the apparatus for this experiment that is shown in the portrait of Rutherford reproduced in Plate I. This long story is given in the hope of conveying what fundamental research is like. It has taken us a long way from Rutherford at McGill in 1902, but we can now go back.

Or shall we first say a word about the gamma rays, which likewise had a long history before their nature was finally settled? They were first so-named by Rutherford at the beginning of 1903, after being called simply "very penetrating rays," and at the time he said that it was hard to decide whether they were a kind of Röntgen ray (X-ray), or electrons with a velocity nearly equal to that of light or uncharged particles. All three would not be turned aside perceptibly in a magnetic field. In 1906 Rutherford was convinced that they were of the nature of X-rays. But it was not until 1914 that the matter was finally settled by Rutherford and me. We measured the wave lengths of the gamma rays by the method of X-ray crystal analysis, which had then been recently discovered, and showed that they were of the same nature as X-rays, but of shorter wave length than ordinary X-rays.

As already stated, Rutherford, with his instinct for correct conclusions in matters of fundamental physics, had become convinced of the true nature of alpha and gamma rays before this nature was definitely established, and argued in accordance with this conviction. Typically, in 1905 he wrote to Otto Hahn, "You saw no doubt that Soddy says the alpha particle is initially uncharged. I will believe it entirely when I have seen it for myself."

THE THEORY OF RADIOACTIVE DISINTEGRATION

This digression has shown, perhaps, how conjecture develops into conviction and conviction into certainty and that apparently simple facts often are not established without long and arduous experiment by men of exceptional ability. It also indicates how Rutherford, having once raised a question, never rested until it was satisfactorily solved. Now let us return to Rutherford and Soddy and their revolutionary theory of radioactive disintegration.

After the two papers on "The Cause and Nature of Radioactivity" which laid down the fundamentals of the subject Rutherford and Soddy took matters further in a paper on "Radioactive Change," published the following year. They again insisted that radioactivity was in its nature something essentially different from hitherto known physical operations. "Radioactivity, according to present knowledge, must be regarded as the result of a process which lies wholly outside the sphere of known controllable forces, and cannot be created, altered or destroyed." They also laid down that there were three parent radioactive elements, uranium, thorium, and radium: it was to be shown later that radium was a radioactive product of uranium. They traced a series of products derived from each parent element by successive discharges of an alpha particle. One of the most striking features of this remarkable paper dealt with the energy of the alpha particle, which, at the time, they took to be a heavy particle with a mass of the order of that of the hydrogen atom. As already described, the identity with the helium atom had not yet been established. The energy was calculated from the velocity and the charge-to-mass ratio, which had been already found by Rutherford. They took the charge to be the same as that on the electron, which, of course, was half what was later shown to be the actual charge. What was in question, however, was a rough value, the kind of magnitude of the energies concerned.

All the details of radioactive changes had not been worked out, but five stages, each attended by the expulsion of an alpha particle, had been traced for radium. This gave a value for the minimum energy attending the disintegration of an atom of radium—five times the energy of an alpha particle.[6] The number of atoms in a gram of radium was roughly known, since the weights of atoms had already been satisfactorily estimated. The total energy expelled during the disintegration of one gram of radium was therefore calculable and it was found that it could not be less than 100 million gram calories, whereas the energy of a typical chemical reaction, such as the formation of water from oxygen and hydrogen, is about 4000 gram calories per gram. These calculations showed clearly that the energies involved in the transformation of the atom itself vastly exceeded the energies involved in the chemical combination of atoms, in which the atoms preserved their individualities. This was a result of fundamental importance.

The rate of liberation of energy by a given amount of uranium, thorium, and radium could be calculated from the ionization produced, since the energy needed to produce a single ion was roughly known. The total energy liberated by one gram of each of these radioactive elements being known from that of the alpha

---

[6] The energy of the alpha particle is not quite the same in each of the five different steps, but for these rough calculations the differences are not significant.

particles, as just explained, the life could be worked out. Calculation led to a half period of a thousand years or so for radium and of thousands of millions of years for uranium and thorium. This, as already pointed out, is why the rate of production, by the three elements in question, of the next member of the radioactive series does not diminish measurably as time goes on.

The last paragraph of the paper on "Radioactive Change" contains a remarkable statement: "All these considerations point to the conclusion that the energy latent in the atom must be enormous compared to that rendered free in ordinary chemical change. Now the radio-elements differ in no way from the other elements in their chemical and physical behaviour. On the one hand they resemble chemically the inactive prototypes in the periodic system very closely, and on the other hand they possess no common chemical characteristics which could be associated with their radioactivity. Hence there is no reason to assume that this enormous store of energy is possessed by the radio-elements alone. . . . The maintenance of solar energy, for example, no longer presents any fundamental difficulty if the internal energy of the component elements is considered to be available, i.e. if processes of sub-atomic change are going on." And this was in 1903! Not until 1942 was atomic energy to be released on a large scale in Enrico Fermi's pile at Chicago; it was 1937 when Hans Bethe worked out the cycle of atomic transmutations that probably maintains the sun's energy. Such is the foresight of genius.

It is worthy of note that about this time a well-known Cambridge physicist, W. C. Dampier Whetham (who subsequently changed his name, for family reasons, to William Dampier), in a letter to Rutherford referred to "your playful suggestion that, could a proper detonator be found, it was just conceivable that a wave of atomic disintegration might be started through matter, which would indeed make this old world vanish in smoke." Elsewhere, he refers to a "joke" of Rutherford's that "some fool in a laboratory might blow up the universe unawares." These suggestions do not, perhaps, seem quite so playful a joke today.

All these notions of changes continuously taking place in the nature of the atom were, of course, in complete conflict with the beliefs generally held by the leading physicists of the time, which were strikingly put by Clerk Maxwell, himself a great innovator and one of the foremost physicists of the nineteenth century. "The formation of the atom is therefore an event not belonging to that order of nature under which we live. It is an operation of a kind which is not, as far as we are aware, going on on earth, or in the sun or the stars, either now or since those bodies began to be formed. It must be referred to the epoch, not of the formation of the earth or of the solar system, but of the establishment of the existing order of nature, and till not only these worlds and systems, but the very order of nature itself is dissolved, we have no reason to expect the occurrence of any operation of a similar kind." This was written in 1875, but it well represents what was being taught at the time of Rutherford and Soddy's work.

ELECTION TO THE ROYAL SOCIETY

The publication of the papers on the nature of radioactivity naturally caused a sensation in the small scientific world of the day, but also created considerable interest in wider circles. In May 1903, just when the paper on "Radioactive Change" was about to appear, Rutherford traveled to England, and Joseph Larmor, the Sec-

retary of the Royal Society, wrote to him shortly before
his departure, "You may be the lion of the season for
the newspapers have become radioactive. I see that you
are again monopolizing most of the Phil. Mag.!", the
Phil. Mag. being the *Philosophical Magazine,* already
mentioned, in which most of the papers on the new
physics appeared, since it provided quick publication.
In June of this year, 1903, Rutherford was elected an
F.R.S., a much desired honor which establishes the recipient as a man of acknowledged position in the world
of science. It may be noted that not quite four years
earlier he had written to Mary Newton, "I have an
F.R.S. in my mind's eye and hope I won't have to wait
too long for it," so that the award cannot have taken
him by surprise. He was thirty-one years old at the time,
a very early age for election; Soddy was elected seven
years later, at the age of thirty-two. During this stay in
England, Rutherford opened a discussion on the emanations from radiative substances at the annual meeting
of the British Association for the Advancement of Science (usually called, without disrespect, the British
Ass), beginning with a brief survey of the known facts
in the field of radioactivity. The crowded audience included many of the leading British scientists of the
day. Oliver Lodge, then a great figure in the world of
science, spoke in support of the theory of disintegration, but he also communicated a written commentary
from Lord Kelvin (born William Thomson), the senior
figure in British physics, who was seventy-nine years
old at the time. Kelvin could not believe that the energy
of radium was derived from atomic transmutation and
suggested that waves in the ether, which was an imagi-
nary substance supposed in those days to fill empty
space and to convey light waves, must somehow supply
it with energy. He also regarded the gamma rays as

merely vapor from radium! H. E. Armstrong, a well-known chemist always reluctant to accept new theories (he could never believe in the existence of ions in liquids, as put forward by Arrhenius), inclined to Kelvin's views and refused to believe in any atomic disintegration. This is cited merely to show that, in spite of the convincing arguments in their favor, the views of Rutherford and Soddy did not command universal belief. It was hard for many of the old school to give up the doctrine of unbreakable atoms. Three years later Kelvin, who said that he thought he had spent more hours than any other person in reading Rutherford's book on *Radio-activity*, was still fighting against the belief in the disintegration theory put forward by Rutherford and Soddy, and its consequences.

This book on radioactivity (spelled by Rutherford with a hyphen at the time) was published early in 1904 by Cambridge University Press. It gave an admirable, simply worded account of the contemporary knowledge of the whole subject, with full and generous acknowledgment of the researches of other workers in the field. It was eagerly received, so much so that a second edition, with considerable additions, appeared in the following year. J. J. Thomson's words well summarized the effect produced by the book: "Rutherford has not only extended the boundaries of knowledge of this subject, but has annexed a whole new province."

THE BAKERIAN LECTURE ON RADIOACTIVE DECAY

After his return to Canada, Rutherford likewise addressed the American Association for the Advancement of Science at St. Louis on radium, with outstanding success. A few months later he was appointed to give the Bakerian lecture at the Royal Society, a great distinction very rarely conferred on a newly elected Fellow. The lecture was founded in 1775 and named after Henry Baker, who provided the funds from which the lecturer was recompensed. Rutherford visited England to deliver the lecture in May 1904. The title of his discourse was "The Succession of Changes in Radioactive Bodies" and in print it ran to some twenty-five thousand words. Much of it was devoted to expounding the fundamental facts of radioactive change, which had already been much discussed. Four elements were taken as being each one the source of a series of radioactive changes—radium, thorium, uranium, and actinium—but it was pointed out since the half period of radium was of the order of a thousand years, any radium that had been there 100,000 years or more ago would have completely vanished, and that therefore the radium itself must be renewed by some very long-lived radioactive substance, an important point. Rutherford argued that uranium best fulfilled the condition of being the parent of radium, but said that there was no definite experimental evidence to this effect. He pointed out, however, that if uranium were the parent of radium, then the amount of radium in different uranium ores should always be proportional to the amount of uranium present.

A little later Rutherford, B. B. Boltwood, and R. J. Strutt, together and separately, attacked this problem of the proportionality of the amount of radium to that of uranium. The most complete results were obtained by Boltwood, who with twenty-one different ores, coming from seven different parts of the world, and containing individually from 75 per cent to less than 1 per cent of uranium, found that the ratio of the amount of radium to the amount of uranium was the same in all of them.

In this Bakerian lecture Rutherford also gave the

mathematical theory of the activity of a substance in which successive radioactive changes, involving both growth and decay, are taking place, and sorted out the complicated series of products from radium, thorium, and actinium. He gave the evidence for the theory of successive changes, that the parent substance produced an element, which in its turn produced another element, and so on, in a family tree. Thus radium emanation, produced by radium, was transformed into radium A, with the emission of an alpha particle, the half period being 3.85 days; radium A was transformed into radium B, again with the emission of an alpha particle, the half period being only 3 minutes, and radium B to radium C, a rayless change with a half period of 28 minutes. These three substances were, of course, present in the active deposit. He also showed that radium C, which emitted alpha, beta, and gamma rays and had a half period of 21 minutes, was succeeded by products of slow transformation, also present in the active deposit: radium D, 40 years; radium E, six days; and radium F, 143 days. Radium D to E was a rayless change; the change of radium E was accompanied by beta and gamma rays, and radium F emitted alpha particles. Subsequent researches somewhat modified the half value periods, but not considerably: thus, for radium D, twenty-five years was found instead of forty years. The "rayless" changes were found actually to be accompanied by beta rays: there are in fact no rayless changes. But general analysis followed the lines established by Rutherford. Incidentally, he showed that radium F was Madame Curie's polonium. This element had also been found by W. Marckwald in association with the element tellurium in pitchblende residues, and called by him radiotellurium. This merely indicates the complications that had to be straightened out.

It was soon after shown that radium F, on the emission of an alpha particle, was changed to a species of lead, which was inactive and the end of the series, a matter to be discussed later.

In a similar way Rutherford analyzed the active deposit of thorium into successive products thorium A, B, and C, and actinium into successive products actinium A, B, and C. Later it was demonstrated that these final products were also forms of lead, thorium C and actinium C being shown to be the final products. It may be said that in this Bakerian lecture he laid precisely the foundations for all subsequent theory of radioactive change.

The Age of the Earth

Another subject discussed by Rutherford on this visit to England was the bearing on the estimated age of the earth of the heat generated throughout the ages by the radioactive elements contained in the earth. Pierre Curie and A. Laborde had found that radium was always hotter than its surroundings, and Rutherford, first alone and then in conjunction with H. T. Barnes, who was an expert in heat measurements with no particular knowledge of radioactivity, measured the heating effect of radium in equilibrium with its products, and of the emanation.

Now Lord Kelvin had calculated the age of the earth from considerations of the time needed to cool from a molten state to the present temperature, the heat, conducted from within, escaping from the surface by radiation. As we go down into the earth the temperature is found to rise systematically, at an average rate of about 1°F per fifty or sixty feet, the gradient varying with the nature of the rock, since some rocks conduct heat better than others. To take an example, in a 9000-foot-deep oil well at Long Beach, California, the temperature of boiling water was attained 7200 feet down and at the bottom of the hole the temperature was 120°C, which is 248°F. This corresponds to a temperature gradient of about 1°F per fifty feet.

From the heat conductivity of the average material of the earth's crust and the average gradient of temperature the amount of heat lost in a given period can be calculated. Kelvin found that to arrive at the present-day temperature between 20 and 40 million years must have elapsed since the earth was a molten mass, and so the earth as a habitable planet could not have existed for so long. He supported this estimate with certain complicated calculations on the effect of the tides in lengthening the day. However, the geologists and biologists who dealt with the evolution of rocks and of different forms of life came to the conclusion that the earth must have existed for a much longer period. There were, then, two quite different schools of thought on this difficult subject. As the great biologist T. H. Huxley amusingly said in 1869, "This result of Professor Thomson's [William Thomson had not been made Lord Kelvin at the time], although very liberal in the allowance of time, has offended geologists, because, having been accustomed to deal with time as an infinite quantity at their disposal, they naturally feel embarrassment and alarm at any attempt of the science of physics to place a limit upon their speculations."

Rutherford pointed out that if heat was being, and had been, supplied by radioactive transformations taking place in the earth, then the earth would not have lost heat as quickly as Kelvin had worked out; clearly if the heat were being supplied rapidly enough, the earth would warm up! He calculated that one part by weight of radium in 22 million million parts of earth substance would produce as much heat as was lost by conduction. In a lecture which he gave at the Royal Institution just after his Bakerian lecture at the Royal Society, Rutherford dealt in a preliminary way with the influence of radioactive heating on the earth's age. Eve records something that Rutherford said about this lecture which shows that he could be tactful when necessary: "I came into the room, which was half dark, and presently spotted Lord Kelvin in the audience and realized that I was in for trouble at the last part of my speech dealing with the age of the earth, where my views conflicted with him. To my relief, Kelvin fell asleep, but as I came to the important point, I saw the old bird sit up, open an eye and cock a baleful glance at me! Then a sudden inspiration came, and I said Lord Kelvin had limited the age of the earth, *provided no new source was discovered.* That prophetic utterance refers to what we are now considering tonight, radium! Behold! the old boy beamed upon me."

Early the next year Rutherford published a popular article—an unusual thing for him[7]—on "Radium—the Cause of the Earth's Heat," in the well-known *Harper's Magazine.* In this he again emphasized, as he had done with Soddy in the famous paper "Radioactive Change," that "It is not unlikely that under the influence of the very high solar temperature, the atoms of the non-radioactive elements may break up into the simpler forms with the evolution of large quantities of energy." He concluded that the sun would continue to supply us with heat for about one hundred times the 5 or 6 million years estimated by Kelvin. This conclusion of Ruther-

[7] Some months earlier he had said in a letter to his mother that he had arranged to write this article "for which I will be paid 350 dollars—pretty good pay."

ford's, given on another occasion, was the subject of a large journalistic headline: DOOMSDAY POSTPONED.

In this article he repeated, with the same arguments that he had used in his Bakerian lecture, his conviction that the parent element of radium was uranium. That *Harper's Magazine* sought and published a review of this kind is an indication of the great popular interest that radioactivity had aroused.

RADIOACTIVITY OF THE EARTH AND ATMOSPHERE

Within the next few years the radioactivity of the earth was the subject of considerable research. R. J. Strutt, to become Lord Rayleigh on the death of his father in 1919, and others after him, found that the available rocks—that is, rocks close to the surface when the earth is considered as a whole—contained an amount of radium relatively so great that, if it existed in the same proportion throughout the body of the earth, the heat generated would be twenty times as great as that needed, according to Rutherford, to keep the temperature gradient unaltered, so that the earth would be rapidly heating. The question of the amount of thorium existing in the available rocks was also investigated. The conclusion was that the uranium (with, of course, its due proportion of radium) and the thorium must be concentrated in a surface layer of the earth some twelve miles thick. The distinguished and highly individual Irish geologist and physicist John Joly, and A. S. Eve, who carried out extensive researches on various problems in radioactivity at McGill, also played important parts in clearing up the problems of the radioactivity of the earth's crust.

An allied problem was the radioactivity of the atmosphere. Elster and Geitel were the pioneers in investigating this, having found in 1901 that a charged body lost its charge rapidly in the open air and a little later that a negatively, but not a positively, charged wire collected radioactive matter from the air, which decayed in activity. In the *Harper's Magazine* article just mentioned Rutherford paid tribute to this famous pair of collaborators, saying that much of our information concerning radioactive substances in the earth's crust and in the atmosphere was due to their "splendid work." Rutherford and S. J. Allen showed that the activity of this substance collected from the atmosphere was mainly due to alpha rays, and in 1904, the year of Rutherford's visit to England which we have been discussing, H. A. Bumstead proved that the active matter collected on the charged wire was the same as the active deposit from radium emanation, mixed with that from thorium emanation. It was to be expected that some of the gaseous emanations from the radium and thorium in the earth's crust would leak into the atmosphere. With a sealed electroscope which could be surrounded with absorbent material it was also shown that gamma rays from radioactive material in the earth's crust were producing ionization. It was not until many years later, 1912 and onward, that V. F. Hess showed, by balloon flights, that ionization in a closed vessel increased at great heights, which gave evidence that ionizing rays were coming in from outer space, the so-called cosmic rays, the subject of much recent research.

Rutherford thus took a great interest in the radioactivity of the earth and atmosphere and was the first to point out the important bearing of radioactive changes on the earth's temperature and the way in which the radium content of pitchblende, for instance, could give decisive evidence as to the age of the earth. The subject was, however, one in which he became incidentally interested rather than one on which he concentrated his mighty powers, and little more will be said of it.

THE RUMFORD MEDAL AND THE SILLIMAN LECTURES

The start of this brief digression was Rutherford's lecture at the Royal Institution in May of 1904, when, to the great interest of the scientific world and the public in general, he raised the question of the age of the earth in the manner that has been described. In June he returned to Canada by way of New York. He was soon to receive a new honor, of which he learned in November, namely the award, by the Royal Society, of the Rumford medal, which is bestowed every second year for outstanding advance in some branch of physics. In Rutherford's case it was stated to be "for his researches in radio-activity, particularly for his discovery of the existence and properties of the gaseous emanations from radioactive bodies." It is, perhaps, worth recording that the medal, which is considered a high distinction, was established in 1796 by that remarkable figure Count Rumford, born in America as Benjamin Thompson, who joined the British ranks in Boston in 1775 and in 1776 hastily left his native land, never to return. He was appointed to a comfortable post in London, and while there engaged in scientific experiments and was made a Fellow of the Royal Society. Later he went to Bavaria, where he reorganized the army and carried out with extraordinary success the task of reducing to contented order a rabble of beggars and vagabonds who were terrorizing Munich. He expressed his principles in the words, "To make vicious and abandoned people happy it has generally been supposed necessary first to make them virtuous. But why not reverse the order? Why not make them happy, and then virtuous?" For his services to Bavaria, where incidentally he made important observations bearing on the nature of heat which are recorded in most textbooks of physics, he was made a count of the Holy Roman Empire and assumed the title of Count Rumford. Rumford was the name by which Concord, New Hampshire, where he spent decisive years of his early manhood, was originally known. Later he returned to England, where he was instrumental in founding the Royal Institution. Finally he went to France, where, to his great discomfort, he married the wealthy widow of the famous French chemist Antoine Laurent Lavoisier, executed during the French Revolution. At the time of his gift to the Royal Society which founded the Rumford medal, thinking of his native land, he presented $5000, a large sum in those days, to the American Academy of Arts and Sciences, intended to provide a reward for important scientific discoveries made and published in America. Such characters as Rumford are sufficiently rare to excuse this digression.[8]

The award of the Rumford medal was accompanied by another distinction that proclaimed Rutherford's growing fame. On November 9, 1904, he told of it in a letter to his wife, who was at the time visiting New Zealand with their little daughter. Having recorded the Rumford award, of which he had just heard, he went on, "It never rains but it pours. On Saturday morning I received a letter from Professor Hadley of Yale asking me if I would deliver the Silliman Lectures at Yale this

[8] For an account of his extraordinary career, see *Count Rumford, Physicist Extraordinary*, by Sanborn C. Brown (Science Study Series, S28, Doubleday Anchor Books).

year. You remember J.J. delivered them two years ago and came over for the purpose, and Professor Sherrington[9] (the physiologist) of Liverpool, last year. It is a great distinction, more especially as the sum paid to the lecturer is 2500 dollars. . . . The fee you will agree with me is not to be sneezed at. It is not often that one can earn a year's salary for ten lectures." The Rumford medal was also the occasion of great celebrations in Montreal, for the distinction brought to McGill University, combined with Rutherford's personal popularity, called for academic rejoicings. Rutherford's accounts in letters to his wife are so characteristic of the man—for he wrote just as he spoke, with the same simple self-confidence and obvious pleasure in success— that they must be quoted. In November 1904, he says, "Cox tells me that a dinner is to be given me somewhere about the time of the presentation of the medal in London.[10] . . . Everybody seems pleased and to agree that I deserved it, which is not generally the case with one's colleagues." The next month he wrote of the dinner, the first sentence quoted showing his usual interest in matters of money, "As I told you Macdonald took over the expenses of the dinner, which was given regardless of expense. . . . After the usual toasts, Cox got up and made the speech of the evening. It was really very clever and not unduly buttery and with a good many jokes. Everyone considers that Cox excelled himself on that

[9] Charles Sherrington was the greatest physiologist of his generation. His book *The Integrative Action of the Nervous System,* published in 1906 by the Yale University Press and based on his Silliman lectures, is a great classic of science. It has been said that he achieved for the nervous system what William Harvey achieved for the circulation of the blood.

[10] Presentation to a representative, of course, as Rutherford was in Canada at the time.

occasion. . . . I talked about twenty minutes and got along better than I thought I would. I think they all considered I made a fair speech. I took the historical order and gave credit to all the people who had worked with me and worked off a few villainous jokes. They received me extremely well and my health was drunk amid much enthusiasm (or at any rate well simulated, if it wasn't real)." He thoroughly enjoyed this kind of thing.

If much attention has been devoted to the year 1904, it is because it was one of the most eventful years in Rutherford's life. He himself wrote from Montreal to his wife, who was still on a visit to New Zealand at the time, on January 1, 1905, "I don't suppose that this year will be quite so full of important happenings as last year for I have been amazed when I reflect on the number of things I got through. There was my visit to St. Louis, followed by the lectures in the States, the publication of my book, the voyage to England and my lectures there, the publication of the Bakerian Lecture and my paper to the Electrical Congress, also the address at St. Louis, and finally the Rumford Medal and the award of the Silliman Lectures." This is a list of awards and publications, but the year also marks the definite establishment, with convincing detail, of the theory of radioactive disintegration, and its general acceptance by the scientific world. In a letter written a few months later he said that he had had to work like a Trojan and never intended to work as hard again in the future, if he could help it.

THE ALPHA PARTICLE

During the time that remained to him at McGill, before he departed in May 1907 for Manchester, where he was to be professor until 1919, Rutherford's researches were mainly concerned with the alpha particle. His determination in 1903 of e/m, the ratio of the charge to the mass, for the alpha particle has already been mentioned. He now engaged upon a more accurate determination, using the alpha rays from radium C, from which they all escape with the same speed, as they do from any single element. The earlier experiments were done with radium in equilibrium with its products, so that there were present alpha rays from radium, radium emanation, radium A, and radium C, all four giving out particles of different speed. As W. H. Bragg had shown, alpha particles have a definite range in air, depending on their initial speed, so that particles from the four elements named have different ranges. In Rutherford's original experiments a thick layer of radium was used, with the consequence that the alpha particles from the bottom of the layer were slowed down by their passage through the layer, so that, quite apart from the four different initial speeds, there was a wide range of speeds of the particles as they left the source. All this made anything in the way of an accurate determination impossible.

A fine wire exposed to the radium emanation, and then allowed to stand for fifteen minutes, during which the radium A decayed to practically nothing, leaving only radium C, furnished a source of particles of uniform speed. A new apparatus, with a fine slit and a photographic plate to register the arrival of the particles, enabled the magnetic deflection to be accurately determined, and a modification of the arrangement gave the electric deflection. Rutherford found a more accurate value for e/m than that of his first determination, but in particular he showed that this value was the same whether the particles had been slowed down by passing through matter or no, which was added proof that the alpha rays were, in fact, particles that preserved their identity whatever their speed. He likewise found that e/m was the same for alpha particles from radium A and radium F, although the initial velocity was different in each case. All this was in the nature of confirmation of his convictions.

FRIENDSHIP WITH OTTO HAHN

An interesting event of 1905 was the arrival at the McGill laboratory of Otto Hahn, destined to receive the Nobel Prize for Chemistry for 1944 in recognition of his pioneering work on the fracture of the atomic nucleus, which played so important a part in the researches that led to the atomic bomb. In 1905 Hahn had already separated out from thorium a new and very active radio-element called radiothorium, which produced thorium emanation. The active deposit from this contained two elements that shot off alpha particles with two different ranges. Rutherford and Hahn showed that these particles had the same mass as those from the radium products. This was only added evidence of the individuality of the alpha particle, but the collaboration is mentioned as an example of Rutherford's power of attracting research students of all countries. Hahn returned to his native land, Germany, after a year with Rutherford, but Rutherford carried on an active correspondence with him until the end of his, Rutherford's, life. Rutherford's letters are, needless to say, full of interesting and stimulating comment on the radioactive themes of the day, but also touch on more personal matters. Thus, in announcing to Hahn in January 1907 his appointment as professor at Manchester, he comments, "The Laboratory is a very good one and also the salary, so I expect to have a good time. I shall be glad too to be nearer the scientific centre as I always feel America as well as Canada is on the periphery of the circle." This was, of course, two generations ago. Hahn's letters to Rutherford have not been made public.

Hahn has, however, recently published an autobiography which contains a most interesting account of his time at McGill and of his relations with Rutherford in general. He records, for instance, that Rutherford would laugh so heartily that it echoed through the whole institute. He tells an amusing story of how a photographer came to the Montreal laboratory one day to take a picture of Rutherford for the famous scientific periodical *Nature* and duly did so in a cellar where the professor sat in front of his apparatus. However, when the plate was developed the photographer was not satisfied with it: he found that Rutherford did not look elegant enough for the special publication in view. Even his cuffs were not showing, as they should have been in those days for the well-dressed man. So Hahn lent Rutherford the detachable cuffs which he, like many men, especially Germans, wore in those days, and in the picture eventually published one of Hahn's cuffs shows very plainly on Rutherford's left hand, which is presented to the spectator. So, says Hahn, I had in the year 1906 the proud satisfaction of seeing my cuffs immortalized in *Nature*.

Rutherford attracted many other very able collaborators to McGill, some of whom have been mentioned. His first foreign student was E. Godlewski, a Pole who arrived at the end of 1904, apparently an able and charming man, who died young and never did anything outstanding. Soddy, of course, was quite exceptional, but there were others of significance. If, among these others, Hahn has been singled out for special mention it is because he was attracted to Rutherford across the Atlantic, because he made important contributions to the study of radioactivity, because he afterward made fundamental discoveries concerning the fracture of the atomic nucleus and because of the lifelong friendship that ensued between the two men.

Another close friendship of Rutherford's was that with the celebrated W. H. Bragg, who was later to follow him as President of the Royal Society. Bragg, who was at the time professor of physics at the University of Adelaide, in South Australia, was nine years older than Rutherford, but did not start research until 1904, when he began investigations on the range of alpha particles, which he showed to be sharply defined. It was his work on these particles which made his name and brought him into contact with Rutherford, their early letters being concerned with preventing an overlap of their researches on the subject. At the time in question their contact was limited to cordial correspondence, but Bragg came to England to take up the professorship of physics at Leeds in 1908, the year after Rutherford became professor at Manchester, when their personal intercourse speedily developed.

During the last years at McGill, Rutherford carried out the measurements of the charge on the alpha particle to which reference has already been made and from this estimated the total number of alphas which one gram of radium sends out per second, namely 250,-000 millions. This makes it easy to understand the heating effect.

A SECOND EDITION OF *Radio-activity*

In 1905 appeared the second, and much enlarged—558 pages instead of the original 382—edition of his *Radio-activity*.* In this second edition Rutherford expressed himself with his usual clarity on several of the most difficult and controversial points in the theory of radioactive disintegration. In particular he said that, taking the view that the alpha particles were projected helium atoms—a point which had not at the time been established beyond question—we must regard the atoms of the radio-elements as compounds of some known or unknown substance and helium. In most of the transmutations a helium atom is projected with great velocity, so that the disintegration is accompanied by releases of enormous quantities of energy. "On this view uranium, thorium and radium are in reality compounds of helium. The helium, however, is held in such strong combinations that the compound cannot be broken up by chemical or physical forces, and, in consequence, these bodies behave as chemical elements in the ordinarily accepted chemical sense." He quoted this passage as expressing his views in a revival, initiated by Lord Kelvin in 1906, of the controversy as to whether radium was an element. Rutherford said in his reply that if radium was a compound of helium it was of a character entirely different from that of any other compound known to chemistry, pointing out in particular that the energy released by unit mass in radioactive change was at least a million times greater than that involved in any molecular change known, and that the

* Hyphenation of radio-activity came into usage between 1903 and 1905.

rate of disintegration was independent of temperature, matters to which attention has already been directed but which can, perhaps, stand repetition. Rutherford also emphasized in his reply the point, made in his book, that the final stable, unradioactive product of the radium series of disintegrations was lead, saying, "I have for some time considered it probable that lead is the end or final product of radium." As we shall see later, this is correct. All the radioactive disintegrations end in a form of lead, and the atomic nucleus, the existence of which Rutherford established in 1911, is, in a sense, a compound containing alpha particles. The nucleus is so well protected from, so inaccessible to, ordinary physical and chemical action, that, to use Rutherford's 1905 phrase, it cannot be broken up by ordinary chemical or physical forces. Rutherford's decisive pronouncements on the nature of radioactive elements, stated in the simplest language, were, then, an accurate forecast of what was later to be proved beyond doubt.

In 1906 appeared another book by Rutherford, entitled *Radio-active Transformations*. This was the official publication, required by the terms of the trust, of the Silliman Memorial Lectures delivered by Rutherford in 1905. Naturally enough, it contained little that was not in the second edition of his *Radio-activity,* but it was written with his usual plainness and lucidity and appeared at the same time in German translation, which had a very favorable reception.

PLANS TO LEAVE McGILL

During his last few years at McGill, Rutherford had several offers of professorships at other universities. In 1905 he received an invitation to an attractive post at Yale, which he did not accept, but seems to have used to get his salary raised at McGill. Posts at Columbia University and at Leland Stanford University were also proffered, but what Rutherford wanted to do was to return to England. There were talks of his taking the professorship of physics at King's College, London, but the laboratory facilities there were inadequate. In the middle of 1906, however, came the offer of the chair of physics at Manchester, which led to a turning point in his life.

The professor of physics at Manchester, called the Langworthy professor, was Arthur Schuster. He had carried out distinguished early work on the discharge of electricity through gases and was well known for research in optics and as the author of an excellent book, *The Theory of Optics,* the first edition of which appeared in 1904. His father was a merchant banker who came to settle in England from Frankfurt am Main, where Arthur Schuster himself was born, so that it need hardly be added that Arthur was a rich man as well as a good physicist, an uncommon combination. He was one of the first to take X-ray photographs in England and was in consequence inundated with requests for help from Manchester medical men. More important for our immediate concern, he designed new physical laboratories, of outstanding excellence for the period, which were opened in 1900 by Lord Rayleigh, but about this time Schuster himself gave up experimental physics. He saw to it, however, that the laboratories were well equipped with apparatus. In 1906, when he was fifty-four, he was contemplating retirement, so that he could devote more time to international cooperation in science and to administration, in particular to that of the Royal Society, of which a little later he became Secretary, an honorable and honorary post of great responsibility, and afterward Foreign Secretary, in which capacity he dealt with the relations of the society with the science of other countries. He had the highest regard for Rutherford and in September 1906 wrote to him saying that he wished to give up his professorship and inviting him to be his successor. A passage from Rutherford's reply deserves quotation, as he expresses his position with his usual frankness. "I was very glad to receive your kind letter in reference to the Chair of Physics at Manchester, as it came at a time when I was seriously considering my future plans. I have had to decide during the past year between the attractions of McGill and Yale University and finally decided to remain here. My chief reason for this step was my hope to return ultimately to England to a position where I would not have to sacrifice laboratory facilities by so doing. The position at King's College seemed to me to invite[11] the probability of the latter.

"I very much appreciate your kind and cordial letter and am inclined to consider very favourably the suggestion of becoming a candidate for the position you propose. The fine laboratory you have built up is a great attraction to me as well as the opportunity of more scientific intercourse than occurs here."

His letter to Hahn, saying that he wanted to be nearer to the scientific center of things, has already been quoted. He repeated the same general sentiment in replying to a great tribute to his work at McGill, both as a supreme discoverer and as a great teacher, which the authorities there paid to him as the time of his departure drew near. On this occasion he wrote to the principal of the university, "the determining factor in deciding to go to Manchester was my feeling that it was necessary to be in closer contact with European science

[11] So given in the printed copy of Rutherford's letter, but it seems probable to me that he wrote "involve."

than is possible on this side of the Atlantic." Conditions have, of course, changed considerably since the days of this pronouncement!

It was in Canada that Rutherford and his collaborators set the science of radioactivity upon a sure and substantial basis, which remains in its essentials the same today. This advance involved a complete demolition of the notions concerning the nature of the atom that prevailed when he started work there. The simplicity and clarity of his exposition convinced the active scientific world of the correctness of the theories with which he explained his pioneering researches; his work in the laboratory showed that he was an inspired experimenter of the highest order. His industry was prodigious. To conclude the chapter with words of J. J. Thomson, "Rutherford's scientific activity was never greater than when he was at Montreal."

Chapter V

MANCHESTER

Manchester, a great industrial and commercial center, was in 1907 a city of some 600,000 inhabitants, begrimed by the smoke of hundreds of factory chimneys. It was a city of grim streets but of warm hearts. An important thoroughfare named Market Street was said to be the most congested street in Europe. All the central streets were at that time paved with great cobblestones, to enable the powerful draft horses that drew the heavy drays and lorries to get a grip with their iron-shod hoofs on the surface. There were few beautiful buildings and not many considerable buildings: the great town hall, built in pseudo-gothic style, was of the prevailing smoke-blackened somberness. The most attractive building to strangers was the Midland Hotel, where, under the management of a charming, most capable Frenchman, Monsieur Colbert, one of the best dinners in Europe was served at a charge of seven shillings and sixpence. Needless to say, there were good restaurants, including a German restaurant, where one could dine satisfactorily at a third of that price.

The city had notable centers of culture. The John Rylands Library, containing many treasured old manuscripts and early printed books, was built in 1899. The Manchester Art Gallery was an imposing building. The Hallé Orchestra and Choir, which were centered in Manchester, were known throughout Europe; the Manchester Royal College of Music, of which Hallé was the first principal, was an excellent institution; and it was in 1907 that Annie Horniman established in Manchester at the Gaiety Theatre, named at an earlier date when the productions were somewhat different, the modern repertory theater. There were also excellent music halls, as vaudeville theaters were called in those days, with much in the way of salty humor and sentimental song for those of less exalted taste. All these institutions, however, were not of much interest to Rutherford.

He took a comfortable house with a pleasant garden in a suburb called Withington, on the outskirts of the city, nearly two miles from the laboratory, which was itself somewhat under a mile from the Town Hall. He traveled backward and forward between his home and the laboratory by tramcar, even after the time, at the beginning of 1910, when he bought a motor-car, a Wolseley-Siddeley 14–16 h.p. H. R. Robinson, who entered the university in 1908 and later was closely associated with Rutherford in research and became an intimate friend, has recorded that "Rutherford evidently liked Manchester from the first, and it is a great tribute to his personality that Manchester took to him so warmly—for he was always very plain-spoken, and Lancashire men, almost as markedly as their Yorkshire neighbors, combine a great pride in their own plain-speaking with an even greater intolerance of plain-speaking in others." Rutherford himself wrote to Boltwood on taking up his professorship, "This is a pretty active place and, but for its climate, has a number of advantages—a good set of colleagues, a hospitable and kindly people and no side anywhere. . . . I find the students here regard a full professor as little short of Lord God Almighty. It is quite refreshing after the critical attitude of Canadian students. It is always a good thing to feel you are appreciated"—the usual frankness. In addition his salary was £1600 a year, with very small income tax—sufficient for luxury, in which he did not indulge, in those distant days.

The new laboratory building, to the design and equipment of which Schuster had devoted so much thought, is shown in Plate V, reproduced from a drawing by the architect. This building contained not only the physics lecture theater, classrooms, laboratories, workshop, and so on, but also the electrical-engineering plant and an electro-chemical laboratory. Nevertheless, the space available for physics was exceptionally large and the equipment was also very good for those days, although not as good as that of a first-class German university physics laboratory of those days. For instance, at the beginning of Rutherford's professorship there were in his laboratory no Gaede rotary mercury vacuum pumps, which evacuated apparatus automatically in a small fraction of the time needed with the troublesome hand-operated pump, although these were in general use in Germany. Later a few jealously guarded Gaede pumps were introduced, but at Heidelberg, for example, such a pump was available to any research man who had proved himself capable. From 1908 to 1914 the average annual grant for apparatus and equipment was £420 a year, but it was a usual thing for research men to build much of their own apparatus. This had its advantages.

FELLOW WORKERS

Rutherford was fortunate in many ways at the start of his professorship in Manchester. Schuster, having resigned his professorship, had taken up the post of honorary professor of physics, in which capacity he rendered all possible assistance to his successor. He provided an annual sum of £350, a generous emolument in those days, for the post of a reader in mathematical physics, to which Harry Bateman was appointed. Bateman was a brilliant mathematician, but it was not until 1910 that he really entered into the work of the department and published two papers dealing with mathematical problems in radioactivity. In the same year, he went to the States and ultimately became professor in the California Institute of Technology, where he died. In 1910 he was followed by C. G. (later Sir Charles) Darwin, who threw himself into the research life of the department and carried out important work, to which reference will be made later. Schuster also bequeathed to Rutherford his young German assistant Hans Geiger, whose name speedily became linked with that of Rutherford as collaborator in research on the alpha particle. Most people today have heard of his name in connection with the Geiger counter. Plate VI shows Rutherford and Geiger in the Manchester laboratory.

Further, Rutherford inherited a young laboratory steward, William Kay, a man of quite exceptional parts who was of remarkable assistance in a variety of ways. He was a great hand with apparatus, knowing the tricks of all the physical instruments then in use, and his expert knowledge found expression not only in setting up brilliant lecture experiments but also in cheerfully rendered assistance to research workers. He was, for instance, highly skilled in the handling of radioactive substances, in matters of scientific photography, and in the preparation of diagrams for publication. In short, he was a great figure in the laboratory all through Rutherford's time in Manchester and after, so much so that when in 1946, nearly thirty years after Rutherford left Manchester, he ultimately retired, the university conferred on him an honorary degree, the only case known to me of such a happening.

There was also an excellent glass-blower named Otto Baumbach, an ultrapatriotic German who was not at all an amiable character like Kay, but was a fine craftsman. Among other things, he made the so-called alpha ray tubes, which were about one twentieth of an inch in diameter and of glass so thin that, when they were filled with the gaseous radium emanation, which could be drawn off from the radium stock, the alpha particles could pass freely through the walls, which had a stopping power equivalent to that of about two inches of air or less. These tubes were a source of alpha particles much used by Rutherford's school in place of radium itself. Their activity, of course, fell to a half in 3.85 days, so that after some days they had to be renewed.

Another piece of luck concerned the radium so urgently needed for his researches. The Vienna Academy had lent a supply of radium bromide for the use of both Rutherford and William Ramsay: Ramsay had got hold of all of this and was reluctant to part with it. The Academy then, in January 1908, lent Rutherford three hundred milligrams of radium, an ample stock. This was later purchased for the laboratory. In addition he received from Paris supplies of pitchblende residues containing actinium and other radioactive elements, so that radioactively he was well equipped.

Again, he had persuaded his old friend B. B. Boltwood, of Yale, one of the pioneers in the study of radioactivity, whose important work on uranium as the parent of radium has already been mentioned, to come to Manchester for the session 1907 to 1908. Together they worked on the rate of production of helium by radium and found experimentally that this rate corresponded closely to that calculated from the number of alpha particles expelled per second by unit weight of radium, supposing that alpha particles were helium atoms. This agreement, then, was a further confirmation of the nature of these particles. Boltwood was of great assistance in handling the stock of radium, being an expert chemist in radioactive matters.

Rutherford soon made his personality felt at the university. At the first faculty meeting which he attended the question came up of certain rooms, belonging to the physics department, that had been annexed by the professor of chemistry in the interregnum before Rutherford's arrival. Opening his speech by banging his fist down on the table, with the exclamation "By Thunder!" —a favorite expression of his, reminiscent of the German *"Donnerwetter!"*—he made it abundantly clear, in his vigorous way, that the rooms must be restored to him and, it is chonicled, finally followed the professor of chemistry to his study, telling him, among other things, that he was a nightmare "like the fag-end of a bad dream." After this there is no record of any attempt being made to get the better of him.

He wrote to his mother at the end of October a letter in his usual lively style which gives us a good picture of his start at Manchester: "I have now been lecturing a month and getting things into shape. I am naturally very busy and as newcomers we shall probably have to do a good deal of dining out. I go to two big dinners this week" (and big dinners were big dinners in Manchester in those days), "one to Mr. Donner—a wealthy merchant here—and one to Professor Schuster, my predecessor, who, unlike most professors, is a wealthy man. Everyone is very kind, and I am enjoying my life thoroughly. I have a good many outside lectures in hand

and give one today at the Manchester Literary and
Philosophical Society. I am lecturing later in London
at the Royal Institution, at Dublin and Liverpool, and
so will be kept busy. I am giving a special series of
lectures on 'radioactivity,' which are well attended."
And, of course, incidentally he was getting research going, so much his daily life that he did not mention it,
any more than he wrote of breathing.

COUNTING ATOMIC PARTICLES: ELECTRICAL AND SCINTILLATION METHODS

His own special research started promptly with work
on his favorite alpha particles. With Geiger he worked
out a method of counting single particles electrically,
which depended upon a process known as ionization by
collision. This phenomenon had been investigated in
the Cavendish Laboratory by J. A. Townsend, a friend
who has been mentioned before in connection with
Rutherford's early experiments in Cambridge. If a high
potential, just below that sufficient to cause a spark, is
applied to a gas at low pressure, negative ions acquire
so high a velocity that they themselves, colliding with
other molecules, produce fresh ions, and so on, the
number of original ions thus multiplying until there
results a relatively large electrical effect. In their counter
Rutherford and Geiger disposed a fine wire along the
axis of a brass tube, this central wire being connected
to an electrometer and the outside tube to the negative
pole of a battery. The voltage was adjusted to be just
less than the potential needed to cause a spark with the
gas-pressure in question, which was about a twentieth
of atmospheric pressure. A source of alpha particles
was arranged at the end of a long (fifteen feet long!)
tube, connected to the counter in such a way that the

particles, which had to pass through a fine hole to enter it, traveled parallel to the central wire. The fine hole was covered with a gas-tight flake of extremely thin mica, since the long tube had to be highly evacuated, to give the particles a free run, and the counter contained gas at low pressure. The source was at such a distance, and the hole so small, that only one particle of every several million fired off by the radioactive source entered the counter. Things had to be arranged so that there were only a few particles a minute to be counted, since the electrometer used was slow in responding and recovering. Later, with an improved type of instrument, the so-called string electrometer, they were able to increase the rate of counting considerably. The "string" was an extremely fine conducting thread, between parallel plates, which responded rapidly to changes of charge. This was the first time that it was proved to be possible to count single swift atomic particles, a definite advance in the study of atomic physics.

The celebrated Geiger counter, which was invented in 1913, worked on the same principle of ionization by collision, but instead of an axial wire used a small rod terminating in a fine point, connected to a string electrometer. The rod was kept at a potential just below that needed to make a discharge pass. The fine point, opposite which was a hole covered with a thin foil for the entry of the particles, much increased the sensitiveness. Naturally nowadays, instead of an electrometer a thermionic valve system is used, by the help of which the momentary electrical jerks may be registered by a mechanical counter or made to work any other desired form of recorder.

The mass of radium in the source, which was far too small to be found by weighing, could be estimated by the gamma ray activity as compared with that of an amount of radium bromide weighable with the necessary accuracy. From these experiments it was calculated that one gram of radium itself sent out 34 thousand million alpha particles per second: in equilibrium with its three products it would, of course, send out four times this number. This was, naturally, a much more accurate determination than the estimates originally made by Rutherford in his first measurements of the positive charge carried by the alpha particles. Rutherford and Geiger also measured with much increased accuracy the total charge carried in unit time by the alpha particle from a specimen of radium whose mass was likewise measured by its gamma ray activity. Knowing the number of particles discharged from the radium, they could find with tolerable accuracy the charge on an alpha particle, as already mentioned in Chapter IV. This charge, positive, came out to be about twice the magnitude of the negative charge on the electron. It was naturally concluded that the charge on the alpha particle must be exactly twice the electronic charge, which was the natural unit. At the time, this measurement of the charge of the alpha particle was more accurate than that of the electron, so that half the charge found by Rutherford and Geiger was taken to be the most accurate estimate of the fundamental quantity e, the electronic charge, and for some years was the standard value. It was later replaced by the direct and very precise determinations made by R. A. Millikan at Chicago.

In the same year, 1908, Rutherford and Geiger developed another method of counting single alpha particles. When alpha particles strike a phosphorescent substance—for instance, phosphorescent zinc sulphide—the glow produced is not spread uniformly all over the surface, but under a magnifying glass is seen to consist of a large number of bright points, flashing up momentarily, as discovered by William Crookes and independently by the partners Elster and Geitel in 1903. These tiny flashes were called scintillations. Crookes devised a little instrument, called a spinthariscope, which could almost be called a scientific toy, to demonstrate the effect. In it a tiny speck of radium was fixed half an inch or so in front of a surface covered with zinc sulphide, which was viewed by a simple lens. The momentary scintillations were plainly visible in a darkened room. It was assumed that each one was due to a single alpha particle. Needless to say, from the figure given for the number of particles sent out per second by a gram of radium, it did not take an expensive quantity of radium to produce the relatively few scintillations per second required for this little demonstration.

Rutherford and Geiger took up this matter as another way in which single particles could be counted—one scintillation, one particle. The experiments must, of course, be carried out in a darkened room by an observer who has been sitting in the dark some time, say a quarter of an hour, to let his eyes become sensitive to small light effects. The investigations showed that the number of particles, as counted by the scintillation method, agreed well with that given by the electrical method. This established the observations of scintillations as not a mere laboratory plaything, but a precise laboratory method. As will be seen, the counting of scintillations was destined to give, a few years later, results of paramount importance.

At about the same time Rutherford made a direct measurement of the volume—very small, of course—of radium emanation in equilibrium with a given mass of radium, from which followed at once the amount in equilibrium with one gram of radium. This could also be calculated from the number of alpha particles given out in one second by one gram of radium, which, as described, had just been measured. The good agreement of the results of the two methods was welcome confirmation of their correctness. Rutherford and Royds also recorded carefully the spectrum of the radium emanation, as mentioned in the last chapter.

All that has so far been described took place in his first year at Manchester, which is an indication of the speed with which Rutherford and his collaborators obtained results. In July 1908 he wrote to Hahn telling him of this work and saying that he had never worked so hard in his life—compare the letter to his wife quoted earlier, in which he said that he never intended to work so hard again in the future! He added, in a letter to Hahn, that "Geiger is a good man and worked like a slave. I could never have found time for the drudgery before we got things going in good style."

THE NOBEL PRIZE FOR CHEMISTRY

In the spring of 1908 Rutherford had received the Bressa prize given every few years by the Academy of Sciences of Turin, in Italy, for the best book on experimental science of any kind. As it was worth £384, he was very pleased. But a greater honor was soon to come.

In November of this year of 1908 the award of the Nobel Prize for Chemistry to Rutherford was announced and in the next month he went to Stockholm for the presentation, an imposing ceremony organized by the Swedish Royal Academy of Science. The other Nobel laureates (as the prize winners are called, from the laurel wreaths with which the ancient Greeks were wont to crown victors in their national games and other men of distinction) present were Lippman, already mentioned; Paul Ehrlich, the great German bacteriologist; and Ilya Metchnikoff, the equally great Russian, who shared the prize for medicine between them. They were entertained at a banquet by the king and queen of Sweden and it is recorded officially that, in replying to the toast in his honor, Rutherford made a "speech partly humorous, pronounced with a simplicity full of grace, and expressing astonishment that he, a professor of physics, had been suddenly judged worthy of a Nobel prize for chemistry." He said, in fact, that he had dealt with many different transformations with various time-periods, but the quickest he had met with was his own transformation in one moment from a physicist to a chemist.

For the customary lecture which he delivered on this occasion, Rutherford took as his title "The Chemical Nature of the Alpha-Particles from Radioactive Substances," no doubt introducing the word *chemical* because of the title of his prize. He went through the history of the determination of the nature and properties of the alpha particle, giving an account of the theory of radioactive transformations that he had put forward with Soddy. Toward the end of the lecture he dealt with the work that he had then so recently carried out with Geiger on the counting of alpha particles by the electrical method and by the scintillation method, pointing out that this was the first time that single atoms of matter had been detected by their electrical and optical effects, and that this was possible only because of the great energy of the alpha particles. He concluded by insisting that it was against all the evidence to regard uranium, thorium, or radium as ordinary molecular compounds of helium with known or unknown elements and remarked, with his usual prescience, that it might prove significant that the atomic weight of many elements differed by four, the atomic weight of helium— as, indeed, it subsequently proved to be. Some days later Rutherford wrote to his mother that he and his wife had had a great time in Stockholm, "in fact, the time of our lives."

THE SCATTERING OF ALPHA PARTICLES

After his return from Stockholm the research of the laboratory on the radiations from the radioactive elements continued with the usual energy associated with Rutherford. Interesting work on the recoil of atoms when they shoot off alpha particles, resembling the recoil of a gun when it shoots off a shell, was, for instance, carried out by Walter Makower and others: Hahn was working on the same subject in Germany. Work on spectroscopy, a subject which had been dear to Schuster, was, too, being carried out all the time in Manchester by experts in the subject, such as W. G. Duffield, E. J. Evans, and R. Rossi, but Rutherford did not take overmuch interest in this.

The most sensational discovery of the Manchester period sprang from certain experiments carried out with Rutherford's pet, the alpha particle, dealing with what is called scattering. When a narrow beam of alpha or beta particles passes through a thin sheet of metal— or, for that matter, of any other solid—it loses its definite boundary. When a flat beam falls on a photographic plate, for instance, the image produced is not the well-defined narrow band that it is when there is no sheet interposed, but is a broader band with a blurred indefinite boundary, as shown originally by Rutherford at McGill. The thicker the sheet, so long as it is not thick enough to stop the particles, the broader and more diffuse the band. This is put down to a scatter of the direction of travel of the particles, which, in their passage through the solid, are turned slightly aside, by repeated encounter with atoms, from the straight paths that they normally pursue. Scattering, of course, takes place in a similar way in passage through liquids or gases, but liquids have to be enclosed between solid plates, which complicates things, and the scattering in gases is, of course, very small.

Many measurements have been made on the scattering of beta particles, but, for reasons that we need not pursue, they were very troublesome and those of the period in question did not lead to any very striking results. With alpha particles things were quite different and the results obtained proved to be of such importance that a little space must be devoted to them.

In 1908 Geiger used the scintillation method to measure their scattering. A narrow flat beam of particles, produced by a suitable slit, was allowed to fall on a screen of phosphorescent zinc sulphide, the whole being enclosed in a vacuum to avoid any scattering by air. When there was no obstacle in the path of the beam the observed scintillations were limited to just the area that particles moving in straight-line paths would strike, as was to be expected. When a thin sheet of metal was put between the slit which limited the beam and the phosphorescent screen, scintillations corresponding to particles turned aside from their straight paths were observed. These were carefully counted, and it was found, as was to be expected, that the number of particles turned aside through a given angle decreased rapidly as the angle increased. The biggest angles observed in these experiments were a few degrees only. Some interesting and important observations were made, in particular that the amount of scattering increased as the thickness of the foil increased and with the atomic weight of the metal. The thicker the foil, the more the encounters; the heavier the atoms encountered, the greater the deviating effect of a single encounter.

THE WORK OF GEIGER AND MARSDEN

The year after, Geiger continued the work with the assistance of Ernest Marsden, then twenty years old, who had not yet taken his degree when he was first called on to cooperate. In one of the last lectures that Rutherford ever gave, of which we fortunately have a record, he narrated, "One day Geiger came to me and said, 'Don't you think that young Marsden, whom I am training in radioactive methods, ought to begin a small research?' Now I had thought that too, so I said, 'Why not let him see if any alpha particles can be scattered through a large angle?' I may tell you in confidence[1] that I did not believe that there would be, since we knew that the alpha particle was a very fast massive particle, with a great deal of energy, and you could show that if the scattering was due to the accumulated effect of a number of small scatterings the chance of an alpha particle being scattered backwards was very small. Then I remember two or three days later Geiger coming to me in great excitement and saying, 'We have been able to get some of the alpha particles coming backwards. . . .' It was quite the most incredible event that has ever happened to me in my life. It was almost as incredible as if you fired a 15-inch shell at a piece of tissue paper and it came back and hit you." For Ruth-

[1] It may here be recorded that when Rutherford spoke in confidence he dropped his voice till it was no louder than ordinary speech, which he probably did in this lecture.

erford the alpha particle was, in the atomic world, a projectile of enormous energy.

Let us consider in a little more detail the events to which Rutherford was referring. For the experiments in question, from which so much resulted, Geiger and Marsden used a fine beam of alpha rays falling on a foil, the thickness and the metal of which they varied. If the foil was thin enough the great majority of the particles went right through, but a few were turned aside through large angles, approaching 90°, and occasionally a particle came back again on the side on which it went in, like a ball bouncing back from a wall so rough that the direction of the return varied. Or so it might at first appear, but they showed that it was not a surface effect, for, as the thickness of the foil was increased, the number of particles coming back increased at first and then became steady. This showed that the effect must be connected with penetration up to a certain depth and so due to encounters with atoms in the body of the metal. Increasing the thickness past the limit to which the particles could penetrate would then, as observed, have no effect in increasing the number of particles coming back. Geiger and Marsden also showed that the number of particles thrown back at a given angle increased with the atomic weight of the bombarded metal, that is, with the mass of the atoms in question.

Now the small scatter of the particles that go through the foil, which was the subject of Geiger's first research, can be satisfactorily explained on the supposition that a particle passing through the metal undergoes a large number of very small chance deviations, in random directions. To illustrate what is meant, consider a simple model consisting of a large number of parallel stout wires sticking out horizontally, so as to act as scattering points for small heavy balls dropped through them. Clearly a ball will be thrown sometimes in one direction, sometimes in the other direction, the chance of a large excess of deflections in one direction being small. Most balls will land more or less directly under the point from which they are dropped, but there will be a small number deflected to each side, tailing off as the deflections get bigger. That is what happens to the alpha particles scattered through *small* angles, up to a few degrees.

Just as the chance of guessing the toss of a coin correctly a given number of times, say sixty, out of a hundred can be calculated mathematically by the theory of probabilities, so can the chance of deflection through a given angle of an alpha particle if it is scattered by a large number of encounters, each of which produces a small deflection. It was found that the distribution of scintillations corresponding to particles scattered through the small angles in question, when a beam passes through a foil, could be satisfactorily explained on such a basis. This is called the theory of multiple scattering, because it assumes that each particle has suffered a large number of small deflections.

Similarly, the chance of an alpha particle being turned through a large angle, approaching a right angle, as the result of a large number of small deflections could be calculated, and it was found to be exceedingly small, while a deflection through so large an angle that the particles came back was as good as impossible on the basis of multiple scattering. Nevertheless Geiger and Marsden found perfectly definite evidence of such large deflections, relatively infrequent as they were. For instance, with a foil of platinum as the scatterer, about one particle in eight thousand of those that struck it were turned through an angle greater than a right angle.

This may appear to be a great deal of, possibly, tedious talk about a trifle, but it turned out to be no trifle. As already pointed out, the observation that the scattering effect increased with increasing thickness of the foil, up to a certain point, made it clear that particles which had penetrated the metal were being turned back. A few unexpected particles might seem to most people no great matter—they might be shrugged off as due to radioactive impurities. But to Rutherford, who saw his favorite alpha particles clearly as little projectiles of tremendous energy, it was a miraculous happening—it was, as he said in the passage quoted, the most incredible event that ever happened to him. How could an atomic force exist large enough to turn right back an atom rushing at a speed of some 10,000 miles a second?—10,000 miles a second, not an hour.

The work of Geiger and Marsden was completed in 1909 and Rutherford, although his mind was occupied by a diversity of other things, long pondered over the results, which struck him as so strange. It was early in 1911, as Geiger relates, that "One day Rutherford, obviously in the best of spirits, came into my room and told me that he now knew what the atom looked like and how to explain the large deflections of alpha particles. On the very same day I began an experiment to test the relations expected by Rutherford between the number of scattered particles and the angle of scattering."

THE EMPTINESS OF THE ATOM

Let us consider what was known of the structure of the atom at that time. In Maxwell's days, at the end of the past century, atoms were thought of as behaving like solid particles, minute billiard balls, and much about the behavior of gases had been satisfactorily worked out on the assumption that they were, in effect, a multitude of tiny solid particles perpetually striking one another and rebounding. Rutherford—educated, of course, in this tradition—said once, "I was brought up to look at the atom as a nice hard fellow, red or gray in colour, according to taste." Lenard in 1903 was the first to show that the atom had an open structure, was mostly empty space. He made use of a cathode ray tube with a very small hole in the side, covered with aluminum foil thin enough to let through the cathode rays—swift electrons—but strong enough to resist the atmospheric pressure, the so-called Lenard window. He found that very swift electrons would go through comparatively thick foils. The number of atoms in a given volume and the size of the atom being known approximately, calculation showed that only if the swift electrons passed freely through the bodies of the atoms could the observed penetration be possible.

Lenard therefore considered that atoms were made up of particles which he called dynamids, each of which consisted of an electron closely associated with a unit positive charge, so that the atom as a whole was neutral. Very swift electrons could pass freely between the dynamids, whose electrical field was very limited in extent. He gave striking expression to his findings by saying that the space occupied by a cubic meter of solid platinum was empty except for the dynamids, which could not take up more than a cubic millimeter, that is, a thousand millionths of the whole. This was the first demonstration of the emptiness of the atom.

A little later J. J. Thomson, more concerned with explaining the periodic chemical properties of the atom, developed a suggestion of Kelvin's, that an atom was a sphere of positive electricity, with electrons imbedded in it in sufficient number to make it electrically neutral. These electrons were arranged in a series of concentric rings in one plane, and the building up of the different rings corresponded roughly to the periodic chemical properties. There had been other attempts to build atoms of positive and negative electricity, but none of them had led to anything precise that could be checked by experiment. The test for a physical theory is "What numerical relation does it lead us to expect? Is this effect confirmed by experiment?" It can be said with some justification that because of this lack of anything numerical that could be verified in the laboratory the average man of science did not take speculations about the structure of the atom terribly seriously. They were interesting, like speculations about life on Mars and other planets, but, like these speculations, did not seem capable of being verified. Rutherford changed that position.

RUTHERFORD'S FIRST PAPER ON THE STRUCTURE OF THE ATOM

Rutherford had been impressed by the ease with which alpha particles could pass through thin sheets of matter, metal or glass, and, referring to this in 1909, said, "The old dictum, no doubt true in most cases, that two bodies cannot occupy the same space, no longer holds for atoms of matter if moving at sufficient speed." His astonishment that alpha particles should be thrown back by encounter with atoms, in a way that could not possibly be explained as the cumulative result of a very large number of small deflections, has already been mentioned. The conclusion to which he had come when he told Geiger that he now knew what the atom looked like was that each of the large-angle deflections of the alpha particles must be due to a single encounter and that the only single collision that could produce such a deflection would be one with a very very small, heavy, highly charged particle. The atom must therefore, he decided, consist of a central particle, very small compared to the size of the atom itself, to permit very close approach, in which practically all the mass of the atom was concentrated. It must have, in the case of the elements used for scattering foils, a large charge, that is, a charge very many times the electronic charge. To render the atom, as a whole, neutral, this central particle, later to be called the nucleus, must be surrounded with a sphere of electrification, very thinly spread, of opposite charge. This was the conception that he elaborated in his first paper on the structure of the atom.

It was to the Manchester Literary and Philosophical Society that Rutherford first gave an account of this theory of the scattering of alpha particles through large angles, which necessitated the nuclear structure of the atom. This society dated back to 1781, the word *philosophical* being used to denote natural philosophy and so being equivalent to the modern *scientific,* as has been pointed out in connection with the *Philosophical Magazine.* The *Memoirs* of the society first appeared in 1789. The famous chemist John Dalton, who laid the foundations of the atomic theory of chemistry, joined the society in 1794, when rooms and a laboratory were placed at his disposal in the society's buildings. He became president in 1817, an office which he continued to hold until his death in 1844, and communicated in all no less than one hundred and sixteen papers on scientific subjects to the society. There is, then, a certain appropriateness in the founder of the new theory of the atom making his first communication on the subject to this local society, which was mentioned by Rutherford in the letter to his mother quoted earlier in this chapter. The fuller treatment appeared two months later in a historic paper in the *Philosophical Magazine* for May 1911. This publication in the Phil. Mag., is the true original source for Rutherford's theory, for of the paper before the Manchester society no full account was printed, only a short abstract!

In this first account of his theory, Rutherford considered a heavy center, later to be called the nucleus, with a charge of magnitude Ne, where e is the unit electronic charge and N is a whole number, surrounded by a sphere of electricity of the opposite kind. At this stage he took it that the central charge might be either positive or negative, for, strange as it may appear at first sight, the deflection of a charged particle—in this case of the alpha particle—is the same for either sign. If the central charge is negative the positive particle shoots past it and is then attracted back, so that it describes an orbit looped round the center, as the orbit of a comet, which is attracted by the sun, loops round the sun. If the central charge is positive it repels the positive particle aimed at its near neighborhood, and so causes it to go back. The mathematics of the path is the same in each case. In this first paper Rutherford says that for convenience the central charge may be taken positive, but he says nothing about electrons in the atom. He was concerned solely with the scattering. For scattering through an angle of, say, $10°$ or more, the alpha particle must approach so close to the nucleus that the chance of a second approach of this kind of closeness can be neglected, as can the effect of the very thin-spread electricity of opposite sign assumed to surround the nucleus. Single scattering alone was in question.

THE RUTHERFORD SCATTERING LAW

Rutherford showed that the path of the alpha particle must be a curve of the kind known as a hyperbola, which is also the path of a comet. The more closely the particle is aimed at the nucleus the more sharply it comes back. In Figure 1 three such hyperbolic paths are

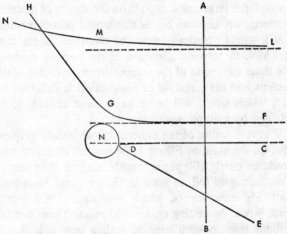

FIGURE 1. *The paths of three alpha particles, one directed nearly at the center of the nucleus, one directed at the edge of the nucleus, and one directed at some distance from the nucleus.*

shown. The straight-line paths of the particles before entering the scattering foil, supposed to be of gold, are indicated by the broken lines running at right angles to AB, which is parallel to the surface of the foil. The circle around N indicates the nucleus, the size of which is taken as given by the nearest approach of an alpha

particle for which the ordinary laws of electrostatic repulsion are obeyed. In the case of CDE, the original
direction of aim runs, as shown, close to the center of
the nucleus (about an eighth of the radius of the nucleus
away) and the direction of the particle is turned
through 152°, so that it comes back on the side by which
it entered. In the case of FGH, the original direction
passes close to the surface of the nucleus and the particle passes through the foil, but its direction is turned
through the large angle of 53°; on the theory of multiple
scattering an angle as big as this would occur so rarely
that it would practically never be observed. In the case
of LMN, the original direction of the particle is about
five times the radius of the nucleus from the center of the
nucleus and the direction of the particle is deflected by
11°, which would still be an angle most unlikely to be
attained by multiple scattering.

To get a notion of the dimensions which are in question, on the scale of Figure 1 the nearest nuclei of gold
would be nearly 100 yards from N, and the thickness of
a medium gold foil, as used in Geiger's and Marsden's
scattering experiments, which was some 3000 atoms
thick, would be getting on for 200 miles. These considerations may make it easy to realize how it is that a
scattering angle in the region of 150° occurs very
seldom.

Rutherford worked out mathematically the probability of a given direction of single scattering with an alpha
particle of given velocity striking a foil of material of
known atomic weight and known thickness. Geiger and
Marsden undertook a detailed investigation to find experimentally how the angle of scattering varied with the
different quantities involved in Rutherford's formula
and found that their results agreed very well with his
theory. It was also clear from Rutherford's theory that,

so long as the thickness of the scattering foil was not too great (that is, was not sufficient to stop the particles) the scattering should be proportional to the thickness, since the number of nuclei that exist as targets increases in proportion to the thickness. The correctness of this prediction was also verified by Geiger and Marsden. On the theory of *multiple* scattering, however, the number of alphas scattered in a given direction should be proportional to the square root of the thickness, another, perhaps unnecessary, indication that large-angle scattering cannot be due to an accumulation of small deflections.

As regards the size of the central charge, Rutherford asserted that it was proportional to the atomic weight, and from this deduced, for instance, that the scattering for gold should be about fifty times that for aluminum, in agreement with experiment. In particular, comparison with experiment gave, as a rough value, the central charge for gold as $100e$. Now the atomic weight of gold is 197, so that it looked as if the central charge, expressed in terms of the electronic charge e, was about half the atomic weight of the element in question. We shall see later that this, though a rough approximation, is not correct. The exact magnitude of the central, or nuclear, charge proved to be fundamental and it was not long before the problem which it presented was beautifully and simply solved.

In 1961 a Rutherford Jubilee International Conference was held at Manchester to celebrate Rutherford's researches there and, in particular, to mark the fiftieth anniversary of the Rutherford scattering law and the discovery of the nuclear atom. All the correspondence and documents were headed with the diagram shown in Plate VII, to indicate the epoch-making nature of

Rutherford's investigation of the orbit of the alpha particle deflected by close encounter with a heavy nucleus.

It may seem surprising that the publication of the paper which put forward, with such strong experimental evidence, the nuclear theory of the atom attracted hardly any attention. Its immense significance was not realized. Not only the general educated world, which had shown such interest in the discovery and early developments of radioactivity, took no notice: the scientific world was equally indifferent. In the world-famous weekly *Nature,* which publishes with excellent judgment the chief scientific news of the day, the only mention was a very brief summary of the Manchester paper, of the same length and style as that devoted to the treatment of all the other papers, many of no great significance, appearing at the same date. Rutherford himself does not seem to have considered his work as the epoch-making innovation that it turned out to be. Even in his book *Radioactive Substances and Their Radiations,* which was completed some eighteen months after the publication of the eventful paper and appeared in 1913, there are only two references to the paper, both where the scattering of alpha particles is being discussed. In this book the word *nucleus* is on one occasion used, but *charged center* is the general designation. Rutherford here definitely declares for a positive charge on the nucleus, and refers to surrounding electrons, but he has nothing to say of the optical or X-ray behavior, or of the chemical properties of the atom, which the nuclear atom was soon to be shown capable of explaining in a satisfactory and surprising manner. It may have been with these great consequences of their work in mind that Rutherford wrote to Geiger years after, in 1932, "They were happy days in Manchester and we wrought better than we knew."

LIFE AT THE MANCHESTER LABORATORY

The discovery of the nuclear atom, which was the greatest among many great achievements of the Manchester period, may be a suitable occasion to pause and look at the general life of the laboratory. The way things went in those days, with the professor devoting practically all his thought and energy to research and in closest contact with all his young collaborators, was something that belongs to a bygone age, which closed with the outbreak of the first great World War in August 1914. The laboratory scene was strenuous, animated and enthusiastic, full of hard work and high spirits. Over all was a feeling of adventure into the unknown.

Rutherford attracted research workers, some of them of outstanding ability, from all over the world: just about half of the men active in his laboratory in the Manchester period had come from overseas to work with him, and of the British investigators less than half had graduated at Manchester. Among those from abroad was G. von Hevesy, from Hungary, who carried out at Manchester remarkable experiments on the electro-chemistry of radioactive bodies and was destined to receive later the Nobel Prize for Chemistry. Of him Rutherford wrote to Stefan Meyer, of the Radium Institute at Vienna, "Dr. von Hevesy will be calling on you on his way to Buda-Pesth. He is an able fellow and has done capable work on the chemical side of radioactivity. He will tell you that he has determined the valency of a great number of the radioactive substances." Later Rutherford became more intimate with Hevesy and more enthusiastic about his achievements, which were of great importance. He kept up a correspondence with him until the end of his (Rutherford's) life. Another man from abroad who became famous was K. Fajans, from Poland, who, after holding academic posts in Germany, went to Michigan as professor of chemistry in 1936. He will be mentioned later in connection with the displacement law. There were many others whose names are familiar to physicists. All these men from different parts of the world, for instance from the United States and Canada, South Africa, and Japan, and from different universities of the homeland, meant a great variety of outlook and lively discussion of questions of all kinds, not only scientific. One learned of the idiosyncrasies of great figures in physics and chemistry from men who knew them personally. There were also from time to time distinguished visitors from abroad, anxious to see what was going on, with Rutherford as anxious to tell them. Bohr has written of "the joy and freshness with which he told about the work in his laboratory."

A great feature of the laboratory life was the tea held every afternoon in the radioactivity training laboratory, at which Rutherford nearly always presided, if that is not too formal a word. He sat at the table with the rest, with his biscuits and his cup of tea, taking part in the conversation, whatever the subject was—and a great variety of subjects came up for discussion, from scientific subtleties to literature and general gossip of the day. Only if radioactive problems of any kind were broached, as, needless to say, they frequently were, did he let it be known, in the most genial and boisterous way, who was boss.

Every day, with rare exceptions, Rutherford rambled round the various rooms where research was going on, visiting each worker, passing a few words if everything was going smoothly, but sitting down on a convenient stool and talking matters over if any unexpected difficulty had turned up or if the next step was in doubt, throwing out suggestions prompted by his ever-active scientific imagination and experimental genius. On one such occasion, when I was working with him on the wave length of the gamma rays, I won a bet from him, perhaps a unique event, as he was not a betting man, but sufficiently typical of the relation between him and his young collaborators for it to be permissible to recount it here. Our apparatus involved a large electromagnet for deflecting out of the way the beta particles from the radioactive source, as otherwise they would affect the photographic plate that we were using to record the gamma rays. One day our plates began to be systematically fogged and Rutherford, sitting on a stool to talk the matter over, made a suggestion as to the cause of the trouble, to which I replied, as one could to Rutherford, "No, I'm sure it's not that." "I bet you a shilling it is," said Rutherford emphatically, and I took him on. Soon after I found the cause of the trouble, which was not perverse physics but simple meddling. The electrical connections for the heavy current for our magnet, and for all other heavy currents used in the laboratory, were made in a special room with voltage bars pierced with holes, into which plugs were inserted. Someone, no doubt busy with other connections, had evidently pulled out by mistake our plugs and then reinserted them, but with the positions accidentally interchanged, so that the direction of our current was reversed, and with it the direction of the magnetic field. The result was that the beta rays were thrown into the plate. We had a laugh about this simple solution of our puzzling problem and Rutherford duly paid me the shilling, which I long treasured.

The physics building included a basement in which were various cellars used for special purposes, in particular as photographic dark rooms. The source of the radium B and radium C which emitted the gamma rays in our experiments was a tube containing radium emanation, the strength of which decays to half value in 3.85 days. This decay meant that, starting with a tube of fresh emanation, the time of exposure for successive experiments had to increase until a fresh source was taken into use. The consequence was that the suitable time for changing the photographic plate, so as not to waste the activity of the emanation, would, every now and then, come out to be midnight or the early hours of the morning. This meant walking in from my rooms and back, a matter of two miles each way, in the quiet midnight hours and descending to the dark rooms, which were among the hot water pipes. A very clear memory of those distant days is the loud chirping of the crickets which lived among those hot pipes. This is just given as an example of the way in which nobody let little inconveniences stand in the way of "getting on with it," as Rutherford would say. H. G. J. Moseley, in particular, would make liquid air at two or three in the morning, if it seemed advantageous.

These cellars, quiet, free from vibration and contamination, were also the seat of certain researches. Geiger refers to them in his lively memories of Rutherford at Manchester—"I see his quiet research room at the top of the physics building, under the roof, where his radium was kept and in which so much well-known work on the emanation was carried out. But I also see the gloomy cellar in which he had fitted up his delicate apparatus for the study of the alpha rays. Rutherford loved this room. One went down two steps and then heard from the darkness [alpha ray scintillations had to be counted in a darkened room] Rutherford's voice reminding one that a hot-pipe crossed the room at head level, and to step over two water-pipes. Then finally, in the feeble light one saw the great man himself seated at his apparatus and straightway he would recount in his own inimitable way the progress of his experiments, and point out the difficulties that he had to overcome. . . ."

A well-known habit of Rutherford's in these Manchester days was singing, loudly and out of tune, "Onward, Christian Soldiers" as he walked about the laboratories. This was a sign of general content and indicated to the knowing that all was going well. He was not always in this mood, but periods of impatience and bad temper were infrequent and did not last long. As H. R. Robinson says, after recording an instance of a temporary tempest, in which he, Robinson, got the better of it, "This did the trick; in a few seconds he laughed, and soon afterwards he was carolling 'Onward, Christian Soldiers' as he went on his round." The word carolling, however, does not perhaps aptly describe the method of vocalization, which had in it an element of grunting.

Rutherford believed in improvised apparatus as long as it worked: the great thing was "to get on with it," without waiting for the delivery of beautifully finished instruments, which, incidentally, cost money. In his earlier days at Manchester many of the electroscopes used for research were made from discarded cigarette tins. Things would have been easier if, for instance, better vacuum pumps and more of them had been available, but possibly his early training had convinced him that simple apparatus would always serve—as it did, but with it the job sometimes took longer to do, and was more troublesome than was necessary. To interpose, if it be allowed, once more a personal reminiscence, I well remember that after I had been in the laboratory for a few weeks Kay, the indispensable laboratory steward, friend of everybody, to whom tribute has already been paid, said to me, "Papa says you'll do," Papa being a common laboratory nickname for Rutherford, derived from a popular vaudeville turn. Fondly imagining that I had said something about physics, at the tea gathering, perhaps, that had struck him as intelligent, I asked Kay, "What made him say that?" "He saw you making that plate-holder out of cardboard, and thought that you made a good job of it," was the reply. Actually, for the purpose in hand, the cardboard plate holder, closed at the front with a piece of black paper, served just as well as a more elaborate and more expensive device.

MOSELEY'S EXPERIMENTS WITH X-RAY SPECTRA

We turn again to the physics that was the essence of Rutherford's life, and in particular to the development of the nuclear atom, the birth of which had caused so little stir. Two men whose work was destined to establish the nuclear atom as of fundamental importance were closely associated with, and inspired by, Rutherford in his Manchester days, H. G. J. Moseley and Niels Bohr. Moseley, killed in 1915 while serving as an army officer at Suvla Bay, in the Dardanelles, had studied physics at Oxford, but, full of enthusiasm for the work being carried out at Manchester, applied to the laboratory and was appointed to a junior position on the staff at the beginning of the academic year in 1910. He was then aged twenty-three. With him came, from Cambridge, Charles Galton Darwin—grandson of the Charles Darwin of the *Origin of the Species*—who, as already noted, was appointed Schuster reader in mathematical physics. Darwin and Moseley became close friends and together they carried out some experiments on the reflections of X-rays from crystals, which convinced them that X-rays did actually behave like light of very short wave length.

Since Röntgen's first discovery, the nature of X-rays had been long in doubt, some considering that they were a kind of particle and others that they were a kind of wave, like light waves, but of immensely shorter wave length. In 1912 Max von Laue, with the assistance of W. Friedrich and P. Knipping, had succeeded in proving, by passing the rays through a crystal, that they were of a wave nature, a discovery of which the fiftieth anniversary was celebrated at Munich in 1962. In the year after Laue's discovery, W. H. and W. L. Bragg showed how the wave lengths of X-rays could be measured by reflecting them at the face of a suitable crystal. Darwin and Moseley had at once taken this up, as just mentioned, and Moseley then settled down to measure systematically the wave lengths of X-rays given out by different elements. The wave length, of course, gives the frequency, that is, the number of vibrations a second, if the velocity is known, and the velocity of X-rays is the same as that of light. The frequency, which for X-rays is in the region of millions of millions of millions of vibrations per second, is the fundamental quantity.

Everybody knows that the visible light which gaseous elements may be provoked to send out (by, for example, passing an electric discharge through a gas, as in a neon or mercury lamp, or by putting a salt in a flame and so producing metallic vapor) consists of monochromatic lights of certain characteristic frequencies, spoken of as spectral lines. The frequencies of the different lines that belong to a given element can be arranged in certain series, the frequencies in a given series being governed by a simple law. This has to be remembered, because it was proved by Bohr to be fundamental for the nuclear atom, as will be set forth shortly.

What Moseley first showed was that the X-rays sent out by a particular element comprised certain characteristic frequencies, called "lines," because, when the X radiation is spread out by reflection from a crystal, just as visible light is spread out by a prism or other device, these characteristic frequencies are made evident by lines on a photographic plate. To use Moseley's own words, "The present paper contains a description of a method of photographing these spectra, which makes the analysis of X-rays as simple as any other branch of spectroscopy." He then compared the frequencies of characteristic lines sent out by different elements, with results of the utmost importance. Let us look back at the way things were done in those days of great, simple discoveries, which will help us to recapture the spirit of Rutherford's lab.

For his experiments Moseley used a wide evacuated glass tube about a yard long, with toy railway lines on which was a trolley carrying a row of blocks of the elements to be examined. Each block in turn was brought into the path of the cathode rays, the impact of which produced the X-rays. These rays came out through a thin window and fell on the crystal used to measure the wave length. It is typical of the scarcity of apparatus, even in Manchester, in these times that the Gaede pump which Moseley used to evacuate his tube was borrowed from Balliol College, Oxford. The apparatus was a troublesome setup to handle, but Moseley was a man of great experimental skill and prodigious industry, who produced his results in surprisingly short time. He worked late at night: in fact, it was said of him that his specialized attainments included a knowledge of where in Manchester to get a meal at three o'clock in the morning. C. G. Darwin states that "he was, without exception, the hardest worker I have ever known." His first work on the subject, carried out in Manchester, was published in 1913. At the beginning of 1914 he went to Oxford, where his widowed mother dwelt, and there he completed the work, as described in a second fundamental paper in 1914.

His great discovery was that a quantity which involved in a simple way the frequency of a characteristic line of the X-ray spectrum of an element increased by a constant amount as one passed from one chemical element to the next one when the elements were arranged in order of atomic weight. What mattered was the number giving the order in the series, not the atomic weight itself. Thus when the elements are arranged in the order of atomic weight, hydrogen is the first, number 1; helium is number 2; lithium is number 3; and so on, gold being, for example, number 79. This number giving the place in the series is called the atomic number. As Moseley himself said of his results, "We have here a proof that there is in the atom a fundamental quantity, which increases by regular steps as we pass from one element to the next. This quantity can only be the charge on the central positive nucleus." That was the essence of his discovery. In an obituary notice which Rutherford wrote when Moseley was killed, he stated, "This proof of Moseley will, in my opinion, rank in importance with the discovery of the periodic law of the elements and of spectral analysis, and in some respects is more fundamental than either." G. Urbain, the great French chemist who was responsible for the discovery of the elements lutecium and dysprosium, wrote of Moseley, *"Sa loi substituait à la classification un peu romantique de Mendeléeff une précision toute scientifique."*[2]

The essence, then, of Moseley's discovery was that if N gives the place number of a given element when all

[2] "His law substituted for Mendeléeff's somewhat romantic classification a completely scientific accuracy."

the elements are arranged in order of atomic weight, then the charge on the nucleus of that element is *Ne,* where *e* is the magnitude of the electronic charge. The charge is not half the atomic weight, as Rutherford originally thought, although this gives a very rough estimate of the value. Thus for gold half the atomic weight is 98, while the atomic number is 79.

Since the frequency of a characteristic line in the X-ray spectrum is connected simply with the atomic number—actually, for those who like exact laws, it is the square root of the frequency that increases by equal steps from one atomic number to the next—we can, from X-ray measurements, see if there is missing any element that ought to be in the series, since in this case there will be an unexpected jump in the characteristic X-ray quantity owing to a missing *N.* This Moseley clearly realized: in a letter to Rutherford he said, "I do not doubt that it will be possible to put every rare earth element into its right pigeon-hole and to settle whether any of them are complex and where to look for new ones." In this way it was found that there were four gaps where, to put the atomic numbers right, there ought to be an element. These four elements were, of course, searched for. The first to be found was number 72, hafnium, discovered in Bohr's laboratory at Copenhagen by D. Coster and G. von Hevesy, the Hevesy who has been already mentioned as a worker in Rutherford's laboratory and subsequently a lifelong friend of his. Hafnia was the old name of Copenhagen. There followed rhenium, number 75, named after Rhenus, the Latin name for the Rhine, and technetium, number 43, named from the Greek word *technetos,* artificial, because it was the first element to become known by being made artificially. The discovery of the last missing element, number 47, has been claimed by several different men or groups, who have given it different names, the most favored of which seems to be promethium. Soddy put the matter strikingly when he wrote, "Moseley, as it were, called the roll of the elements, so that for the first time we could say definitely the number of possible elements between the beginning and the end, and the number that still remained to be found."

So now, as the result of work carried out by Moseley in Rutherford's Manchester laboratory and confirmed beyond doubt by the continuation of this work at Oxford, it was known that it was the size of the charge on Rutherford's nucleus, and nothing else, that determined the chemical properties of the element. Meanwhile, another simple triumph for the nuclear atom had been won, that is, another triumph for Rutherford.

In 1911 Soddy had pointed out that when an element sent out an alpha particle it became a new element with the chemical properties pertaining to two places earlier in the periodic table, in which the elements are arranged in order of atomic weight. In 1913 Soddy; Kasimir Fajans, whose work in Rutherford's laboratory has been already mentioned; and A. S. Russell, another Rutherfordian, all independently remarked that when an element sent out a beta particle it transformed into an element with the chemical properties of one place later in the table. This effect of the loss of an alpha or of a beta particle, which is known as the Displacement Law, fitted in precisely with Moseley's discovery of the virtue of the atomic number. If the particles came from the nucleus, loss of an alpha particle, with two units of positive charge, would lessen the atomic number by 2, and *loss* of a beta particle, with one unit of negative charge, equivalent to a *gain* of one unit of positive charge, would increase the atomic number by 1. This discovery was clear proof that the particles in question came from the nucleus, which was thus the seat of radioactivity. It confirmed the supreme part played by the charge on the nucleus.

BOHR APPLIES THE QUANTUM THEORY TO ATOMIC STRUCTURE

We must now turn to Niels Bohr, who first showed the wide possibilities of the nuclear scheme of the atom in fields other than radioactivity. Bohr had met Rutherford in Cambridge in 1911, some months after the publication first setting forth the nuclear theory, and, fired by the contact, he arranged to join the research group at Manchester early in the next year. Writing of this nearly fifty years later, Bohr said, "In those days many young physicists had gathered round Rutherford, attracted by his genius as a physicist and by his unique gift as a leader of scientific cooperation," another tribute to Rutherford's gift for inspiring those working with him. Bohr saw at once that, while radioactivity was bound up with the nucleus, the ordinary chemical and physical properties of matter must be an affair of the system of electrons surrounding the nucleus, and he proceeded to show how these properties could be explained.

Bohr's scheme was based on the fundamental discovery of Max Planck, first announced many years earlier, that radiation, such as light, was emitted not continuously, as seemed natural, but in little packets of radiant energy, which he called quanta (singular, quantum). There is a temptation to speak of atoms of radiant energy or atoms of light energy, but the fundamental thing about the quantum of radiant energy is that its size depends upon the frequency of the radiation in question. In fact, the size of the quantum of energy of a particular radiation is the frequency of the radiation multiplied by a very very small number, always denoted by *h,* called *Planck's constant.* It is for this reason that the frequency was said earlier to be the fundamental characteristic of a radiation. Thus the quantum, the grain of energy, so to speak, of X-rays of a certain frequency is very much larger than the quantum which is characteristic of a particular kind of visible light, say the green line of the mercury discharge lamp. It is as if we could only buy things in fixed units of price, but that the minimum price varied with the kind of thing— squashes by the ten cents' worth; chickens by the dollar's worth, no fractions of dollars being allowed; watches by the ten dollars' worth, only multiples of ten dollars being allowed; diamonds by the hundred dollars' worth. Thus 12 quanta of diamonds would represent $1200; 12 quanta of squashes would represent $1.20. These things have been chosen as getting smaller as the unit of price rises, in the same way that, as the wave lengths get smaller (that is, as the frequency rises), the size of the quantum of energy rises.

This conception of radiant energy in packets, the size of which is proportional to the frequency, may seem a very strange assumption, but it is deeply involved in all modern atomic theory. It is, of course, no objection to say that we know we can alter the intensity of light as gradually as we like, any more than it is an objection to the atomic theory to say that we can cut up a solid into any weight that we like: the quantum and the atom, the unit of radiation and the unit of mass, are much too small for us to detect them by ordinary measurements. There is no reason why radiant energy should not be in little parcels, or "light darts" as they have been called by Einstein. But it may well be asked why the size of the energy packet should be proportional to the frequency. The answer is the usual one in matters of physical theory—*it works.* On the basis of this assumption a great variety of fundamental results have been calculated which experiment shows to agree precisely with theory.

As a matter of incidental interest, Planck originally put forward the quantum theory to explain the relative energies of lights of different frequencies radiated from a hot solid with no prejudices. A black body absorbs completely all frequencies of radiation, all colors, without prejudice, and similarly a black body, when heated, sends out radiation of all frequencies without prejudice. Planck derived from his light-packet assumption a formula which gave precisely the relative amount of energy of each frequency in what is known as "black body radiation." Formulae based on the old assumption of the continuous nature of light energy gave results widely different from experiment.

When it was first published, in 1901, the quantum theory attracted little attention. For instance, in the 1911 edition of the *Encyclopædia Britannica,* which treats contemporary physics in an excellent and authoritative manner, Planck's formula is cited as giving a good representation of the distribution of energy in black-body radiation, as found experimentally, but no mention is made of the quantum theory, on the basis of which the formula was derived. Einstein had shown that the quantum theory could explain fundamental observations in the field of photoelectricity—the release of electrons by light—and specific heat, but nevertheless the notion of the quantum was too strange, too novel, to be generally accepted. It was Bohr's work that forced physicists and chemists to realize that quantum theory was of paramount importance.

What was the essence of Bohr's epoch-making work on the nuclear atom? It dealt with the behavior of the atomic electrons and embodied a fundamentally new principle, involving the quantum theory. On this basis the frequencies of the different spectral lines—that is, of the different kinds of monochromatic light—sent out by an atom suitably provoked, could be exactly calculated. These frequencies of the different lines, which can be roughly compared to the frequencies of the different tones given out by a plucked string, had been shown to be connected by numerical laws, of which Balmer's Law for the lines of the hydrogen spectrum is a famous example, but no one had been able to find any theoretical explanation for these laws.

THE HYDROGEN SPECTRUM

The hydrogen spectrum, which is the simplest type of spectrum, is of such great importance for Bohr's work that it may be well to say a word about it. A glowing solid—for instance, white-hot iron—gives out visible light of all frequencies; a gas at low pressure through which an electric discharge is passing gives out sharp spectral lines, which represent certain well-defined frequencies. The explanation is this. In a solid the atoms are so close together that they interfere with one another, jostle one another so that they cannot express themselves by the radiations characteristic of their natural undisturbed mode of behavior. With the gas in the discharge tube the atoms are widely separated and their radiation is characteristic of their structure. The hydrogen atom is the simplest atom and it was found by J. J. Balmer that the frequencies of certain lines in its spectrum obeyed a very simple law, being proportional to $\frac{1}{2^2} - \frac{1}{3^2}$, $\frac{1}{2^2} - \frac{1}{4^2}$, $\frac{1}{2^2} - \frac{1}{5^2}$ and so on, the number which is squared in the second term increasing by 1 for each successive line. Thus the frequencies in the Balmer series are proportional to $\frac{1}{4} - \frac{1}{9} = 0.1388\cdots$, $\frac{1}{4} - \frac{1}{16} = 0.1875$, $\frac{1}{4} - \frac{1}{25} = 0.2100$, $\frac{1}{4} - \frac{1}{36} = 0.2222\cdots$ and so on. The lower frequencies are in the red end of the spectrum and the highest crowd up to a limit beyond the violet, a limit given by $\frac{1}{4}$. That there is such a crowding up can easily be seen from the formula, for whereas the difference of frequency between the first two lines is proportional to $0.1875 - 0.1388 = 0.0486\cdots$, the difference between tenth and the eleventh line is $0.0103\cdots$, and so on.

The numbers given by the formula just explained, $\frac{1}{2^2} - \frac{1}{n^2}$, are, of course, not the frequencies but are proportional to the frequencies. What was originally used to denote the frequencies was the inverse of the wave length—i.e., the number of waves in the length of a centimeter, which was called the wave number. It has to be multiplied by the velocity of light, which is the number of unit lengths traversed per second, to give the frequency. J. R. Rydberg, a Swede who died in 1919, went fully into the structure of various spectra and showed the importance of the constant which has to be used as a multiplier of $\frac{1}{2^2} - \frac{1}{n^2}$ to give the wave numbers. This constant is accordingly always called Rydberg's constant, or Rydberg's number. It is 109,677 (leaving out a decimal fraction which has been worked out from very accurate observations), so that, as anyone with the curiosity to check can work out, the wave number of the first line of the Rydberg series is, to five figures, 15233.

The hydrogen spectrum comprises other series of a similar nature to Balmer's series, but as they can be

PLATE VI. Geiger and Rutherford in the Manchester laboratory. The circular instrument is an electrometer of the period.

JUBILEE INTERNATIONAL

September 4th to 8th, 1961

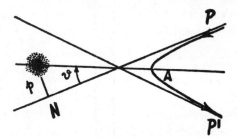

THE UNIVERSITY

PLATE VII. The design used in all the correspondence and documents of the conference held at Manchester in 1961 to celebrate the 50th anniversary of the discovery of the nuclear atom. The full heading was *Rutherford Jubilee International Conference* and *Physics Department, The University, Manchester, England.*

PLATE VIII. Rutherford holding in his hands the apparatus with which the artificial disruption of the nucleus was first demonstrated. (The Cavendish Laboratory, Cambridge)

PLATE IX. Cloud chamber photograph by Blackett showing the disruption of the nitrogen nucleus by an alpha particle.

PLATE X. The apparatus of Cockcroft and Walton, with which high voltage particles were first made to effect artificial disintegration of the atomic nucleus. (The Cavendish Laboratory, Cambridge)

PLATE XI. Photograph of Rutherford taken outside the Cavendish Laboratory in 1934.

PLATE XII. Cloud chamber photograph by Dee and Walton, showing the alpha particles produced by bombarding lithium with accelerated protons.

explained on similar lines it is not necessary to discuss them here.

Before Bohr there had been many unsuccessful attempts to explain the straightforward Balmer series. The fundamental trouble was a simple one. A light of any particular frequency, a monochromatic light, as it is called, is an electromagnetic wave of a simple character, in which the strength of the electric and magnetic force varies periodically, just as does the displacement of a pendulum bob. On the theory that was universally accepted at the time, an electric charge moving periodically, that is, in a manner that repeated itself with the frequency characteristic of the wave, was needed as the source of such a wave. The charge in question must be one of the electrons in the atom and the simplest thing was to suppose it to be going round and round with a frequency corresponding to that of the light. But here came in the difficulty that stumped all the theorists. The moving electron, by sending out light, was losing energy all the time and consequently must revolve more and more slowly as time went on, with a corresponding diminution of the frequency. The simplest case, that of the atom of hydrogen, with one electron, should, on this basis, give out a continuous range of frequencies, but it does not—it gives out only certain definite well-separated frequencies, connected by simple laws. How was the fact that an electron going round in an orbit did not apparently lose energy to be explained?

Bohr did not explain it; he just boldly said that the electron moving in an *atomic* orbit did not radiate! The laws of electromagnetism that explained perfectly large-scale happenings, such as the behavior of electric waves used in wireless telegraphy, did not, he asserted, apply to atoms, which had rules of their own. This, after all, was what Planck had asserted: that when you came down to atomic processes the laws that treated the emissions of radiation as a continuous process did not apply.

To take an analogy from real life, the world at large is made up of families—atoms—but it may be asserted, or at any rate hoped, that the laws that govern public and business activities, large-scale nonatomic happenings, do not apply within families.

BOHR'S MODEL OF THE ATOM

Bohr adopted Rutherford's nuclear atom, considering the nucleus as being surrounded by electrons circulating in orbits, like planets round the sun, and governed by the ordinary laws of electrical attraction, just as planetary orbits are governed by gravitational attraction. He made, however, three assumptions that were quite against the accepted—or classical, as they are often called—laws of electromagnetism. The assumptions were:

First of all (as has been stated) that electrons circulating in these orbits did not radiate. Secondly, that of all the infinite variety of orbits that were permitted by the classical laws, only certain widely separated ones were actually possible, these possible ones being determined by a special quantum condition. An atom in which the electrons were all circulating steadily in orbits allowed by this condition was said to be in a stationary state. Various definitely different stationary states could occur, according to which of the permitted orbits were actually occupied: if in a sparsely inhabited country automobiles are only allowed to drive along certain roads, this does not mean that all the legal roads must necessarily have traffic on them. To each stationary state would belong a certain energy, which could be calculated by Bohr's method.

The third assumption was that the atom sent out radiation only when it passed from one stationary state to another—the simplest case being when one electron ceased to occupy one of the legal quantum orbits and adopted another. The frequency of the radiation was given by the difference of energy between the two stationary states in question, it being assumed that h times the frequency was equal to the difference of energy. It will be remembered that h is Planck's constant.

The scheme was open to the criticism that classical laws were used when it suited, as in finding the general nature of the orbits, and, on the other hand, were thrown aside in the three essential assumptions that have been given. The wonderful thing about Bohr's theory was that it worked, which is all that can be demanded of any physical theory. It not only gave the laws that had been experimentally found to connect the frequencies of the lines in the different series of the hydrogen spectrum, which it might have been said that the assumptions had been engineered to produce, but it gave exactly the magnitude of the physical constant, Rydberg's constant, that fixed the precise values of the frequencies. This constant, on Bohr's theory, involved the value of the charge and of the mass of the electron, the value of Planck's constant $h,$ and the value of the velocity of light, so it could hardly be luck that gave it exactly the right value.

REACTION TO THE BOHR THEORY

Nevertheless, there were many doubters. A typical reaction at the time was that of Lord Rayleigh, the great physicist who had received the Nobel Prize and had been President of the Royal Society. His son records that he asked his father if he had seen Bohr's first paper on the hydrogen spectrum, which had just appeared at the time of the question. The father replied, "Yes, I have looked at it, but I saw it was no use to me. I do not say that discoveries may not be made in that sort of way. I think very likely they may be. But it does not suit me." This was fair enough, merely saying that he did not like that way of going about it to produce a new theory. But the celebrated P. H. Zeeman, whose name is familiar to all physicists by the Zeeman effect and who knew all about spectra, two years after the publication of Bohr's papers dismissed in a line the discoveries which they recorded. O. W. Richardson, who, like Zeeman, received the Nobel Prize for Physics, in a book published at about the same time, devoted little attention to Bohr's work, but he did say that, although the assumptions were against the accepted views, so were those required to account for the distribution of energy in temperature radiations, for which Planck's original theory was devised. There was, then, no question of Bohr's theory being at once widely recognized for the masterpiece that it was, any more than there was of Rutherford's nuclear atom being acclaimed as an epoch-making advance. It took time for physicists to get used to these novel modes of approach, which may comfort the many young men who feel that their fundamental work is not properly appreciated.

Rutherford wrote to Bohr on the appearance of his first paper, "Your ideas as to the mode of origin of the spectra in hydrogen are very ingenious and seem to work out very well; but the mixture of Planck's ideas and the old mechanics makes it very difficult to form a physical idea of what is the basis of it all. There appears to me to be one grave difficulty in your hypothesis, which I have no doubt that you fully realise, namely, how does an electron decide what frequency it is going to vibrate at when it passes from one stationary state to the other? It seems to me that you have to assume that the electron knows beforehand where it is going to stop." This thinking of the electron as a person, a friend, though not such a close friend as the alpha particle, is typical of Rutherford's point of view. The criticism was a just one, drawing attention to the mixture of classical laws and anticlassical assumptions to which reference has already been made.

One man who at once recognized the fundamental importance of Bohr's work was Moseley, who wrote to Rutherford from Oxford at the very beginning of 1914, "Here there is no one interested in atom building. I should be glad to do something towards knocking on the head the very prevalent view that Bohr's work is all juggling with numbers until they can be got to fit. I myself feel convinced that what I have called the 'h' hypothesis is true, that is to say one will be able to build atoms out of e, m and h and nothing else besides."

Soon after his first paper, which dealt with the nucleus with one electron, typified by the hydrogen atom, Bohr considered the general atom, with rings of electrons round the nucleus, building up systems to correspond to the groups of elements in the periodic table. He thus brought the nuclear atom into chemistry, where it was later to play a dominant role. He indicated that it was the inner rings of electrons that were concerned in the emission of X-rays. He also considered in a general way the combination of nuclear atoms to form molecules. The chemical and X-ray aspects were speedily developed in Germany by an old Heidelberg friend of mine, Walther Kossel.

Lest I may be considered as wandering from my subject, Rutherford, let me stress that this development of the nuclear atom by Bohr proved to be a wonderful support of Rutherford's conception, in showing how much wider its scope was than Rutherford had originally suggested. The chemical, the optical, the X-ray properties of the atom had never been contemplated by Rutherford as capable of explanation in terms of the nuclear model. The year 1913, in which Bohr published his first papers on the subject, ranks with 1911, in which Rutherford first put forward his theory, as the date of the foundation of the nuclear atom. Rutherford and Bohr became close friends and Bohr's tribute to Rutherford, entitled "Reminiscences of the Founder of Nuclear Science and of Some Developments Based on His Work," first published in full in 1961, the year before Bohr died, is full of intimate and touching memories.

THE EXISTENCE OF ISOTOPES

The years 1911 to the outbreak of the First World War in 1914, which changed the face of civilization, were full of excitement for physicists, and another discovery which came to a head in 1913 was of prime importance for Rutherford's nuclear atom. This discovery was that elements could exist having identical chemical properties but different masses, which means, in terms of the Rutherford atom, that nuclei having the same charge might have different masses. Such elements are called isotopes, from the Greek words *isos,* equal, and *topos,* place, because they have the same place in the periodic table, in which elements with particular chemical properties occupy particular places.

It had long puzzled men of science that the atomic weights were not multiples of a simple number—say, the mass of the hydrogen atom—but terminated in odd fractions—thus the atomic weight of oxygen being taken as exactly 16, that of chlorine is 35.457 and that of silver 107.880. It was, until the times that we are considering, generally believed that the atoms of a particular element were all strictly identical, had all the same mass, as well as the same chemical properties. In 1886, however, the famous chemist William Crookes had doubted this: to use his actual words, "It may well be questioned whether there is an absolute uniformity of the mass of every ultimate atom of the same chemical element. Probably our atomic weights merely represent a mean value around which the actual atomic weights of the atoms vary within certain narrow limits. . . . This may seem an audacious speculation, but I do not think it beyond the power of chemistry to test its feasability." This speculation, for at the time it was no more, turned out to be true.

The evidence for the existence of isotopes came from two fields, one being Rutherford's happy hunting ground of radioactivity and the other J. J. Thomson's delight, the discharge of electricity through gases. As a typical example from radioactivity, it was found impossible to separate radiothorium from thorium by chemical means, although their radioactive properties showed them clearly to be different, and the atomic weight of thorium was 232 while that of radiothorium 228. In general, different radioactive behavior can be shown by elements of the same chemical properties, which means the same atomic number, which in its turn means the same nuclear charge, while the different radioactive behavior means different nuclear constitution, which can only mean different nuclear masses. It has already been pointed out that the displacement law showed that radioactivity was a nuclear property.

Let us consider a simple case. Three consecutive radioactive products can be produced by the discharge of an alpha particle, followed, one after the other, by the discharge of two beta particles. The loss of the two units of positive charge that belong to the alpha, followed by two separate single losses of a unit of negative charge, puts the atomic charge back where it was, since the loss of a negative charge is equivalent to the gain of a positive charge, but the nuclear mass is about four units less, since the alpha has a mass of four units and the mass of an electron is, by comparison, negligible. Same nuclear charge means same chemical properties, but different nuclear mass means different nuclear make-up and different radioactive properties.

The other proof that atoms of the same chemical nature could have different masses came from the study of the electrical discharge in gases, which allows a beam of positively charged atoms to be produced in an exhausted tube. In Chapter III something has been said of the deflection of a beam of charged particles by an electric and by a magnetic field. J. J. Thomson showed that by using magnetic and electric fields, so disposed as to produce simultaneous deflections in directions at right angles to one another, it was possible to find the mass of the charged atoms in the positive beam. In 1913 J. J. Thomson and F. W. Aston, examining by this method the gas neon, a very pure sample, found that, while the main part of the gas had atomic weight 20, there was a small fraction of the gas with atomic weight 22. The atomic weight of ordinary neon is 20.183. After the First World War, Aston, working in Rutherford's laboratory in Cambridge, developed an apparatus called the mass spectrograph by which he determined the masses of the majority of the elements and showed that the existence of isotopes was quite general. Something will be said of this famous work of Aston's in the next chapter. For the development of

Rutherford's atom the independence of nuclear mass and nuclear charge was of prime importance.

Rutherford summed the matter up with his usual straightforward clarity when he said in a lecture at Sydney, in 1914, "There may be two pieces of lead which look exactly the same and yet their physical qualities may be quite different. That may not be believed now, but it will be later." Later (that is, now) we know that four different isotopes of lead occur in nature. If further examples are desired, chlorine, of atomic weight 35.457, is a mixture of two isotopes, respectively of mass 33 and 37, while the rare gas xenon, of atomic weight 131.30, has nine isotopes, of mass 132, 129, 131, 134, 136, 130, 128, 126, and 124, the order in which they are given being that of the quantities in which they occur, 132 being the most plentiful and 124 the least plentiful.

ACTIVITIES AT THE LABORATORY

In 1914, then, Rutherford was at the height of his activity. At the beginning of the year his outstanding services to science had received official recognition by the award of the honor of knighthood, so that he became Sir Ernest Rutherford. The work of Moseley and of Bohr, both inspired by his invigorating influence, had indicated that the nuclear atom was the start of a new era in the history of physics—and of chemistry. The laboratory at Manchester was a fertile hive of activity, concerned with many matters intimately connected with the atom and its radiations. Even the spectroscopist E. J. Evans was engaged on very accurate measurements of the wave length of spectral lines of hydrogen and helium which turned out to offer strong support for Bohr's theory of spectra, and so for his theory of

atomic structure. James Chadwick, who was later to
work again with Rutherford at the Cavendish Laboratory at Cambridge and was to gain the Nobel Prize for
his discovery of the neutron, had gone to Germany to
work with Geiger there, but work which he had done at
Manchester with A. S. Russell on gamma rays first appeared in 1914. He had been much engaged with these
rays. Marsden was busy with alpha particles, showing
in particular that hydrogen nuclei, struck by them, went
far beyond the range of the particles themselves. H. R.
Robinson was hard at work on the energies of the different kinds of beta rays emitted by certain radioactive
elements. W. Makower, H. Richardson, H. P. Walmsley, A. B. Wood, and others were all occupied with
problems in radioactivity. Rutherford himself was taking the liveliest and most stimulating interest in all these
problems, to the solution of some of which he set his
name with that of his collaborator, but even to those on
which his name did not appear he had generally made
essential contributions. His whole time was taken up
with the activities of the laboratory. It was about this
time that he said to Harold Robinson, "Robinson, you
know, I *am* sorry for the poor fellows that haven't got
labs. to work in!"

I, who, as John Harling Fellow, was working with
him at the time on gamma rays, was witness of an in-
cident which illustrates his attitude. There was working
in the laboratory at the time a foreign lady, of no particular distinction as a physicist, who was somewhat of
a man-hater and consequently would never appeal to a
man for help. She had a bottle of a poisonous gas,
sulphur dioxide, closed with a screw tap which had become stuck. Not being able to loosen it, and being un-
willing to ask a man for aid, she took it downstairs to a
small room and did something to the tap that caused

it to open suddenly, with the result that the gas rushed
out and she was rendered unconscious. Luckily she was
found, on the floor, in time and revived. The next day
I happened to be sitting with Rutherford in his room,
talking over some aspect of our work, when there was
a knock, the door opened, and Miss Bauer (let us call
her), for whom he had sent, appeared. "What's this
I hear, Miss Bauer," he said, "what's this I hear? You
might have killed yourself." "Well, if I had," she replied sourly, "nobody would have cared." To this Rutherford responded incisively, "No, I daresay not, I daresay not, but remember I've no time for inquests!" To
judge by the lady's face, this was hardly the reception
she expected for her remark, but I am convinced that
Rutherford was more or less in earnest at the moment.
To have to spend a morning away from the laboratory
over the clumsiness of Miss Bauer, was, in spite of his
kind heart, something that he could not contemplate
with indifference.

In August 1914 the British Association for the Advancement of Science was to meet in Melbourne, Australia, and Rutherford left England in good time, for, of
course, in those days the journey had to be made by
sea and took about six weeks. Moseley and his mother,
who were going to attend, started also in June. Few
people, if any, in England, can have had any notion
that war was imminent. In Germany at that time people
took the threat of war more seriously. When I was at
Heidelberg in 1911, the Agadir crisis took place, which,
as subsequently appeared, nearly led to a European war.
I was sitting in a café with German friends, when one
of them asked me if I was going back to England.
"Why?" I queried. "There seems to be danger of war,"
he replied, to which I answered, "Don't be so silly. We
are not living in the Balkans! You don't really think

that the people sitting round here are going into the field to shoot at other people like them?" I thought that I was being very worldly-wise in the face of an out-of-date attitude. If no one in England took the threat of war seriously, and quite a number did not take the nuclear atom seriously, it is certain that not a single soul thought that there could ever be the slightest connection between the two, as, alas, we now know to be the case.

A VISIT TO MELBOURNE AND NEW ZEALAND

War broke out on August 4, 1914, but did not affect the meeting at Melbourne. On August 18 Rutherford opened a discussion there on the structure of atoms and molecules, a discussion of which, strange to say, no proper report exists, only an abstract, in which Rutherford's address occupies little more than a page. He spoke of large single scattering of the alpha particle, mentioning the important fact that, in C. T. R. Wilson's cloud chamber method of rendering visible the tracks of ionizing particles in gases, which will be described in the next chapter, certain of the alpha ray tracks showed sharp bends. This, of course, supported his theory. He emphasized the importance of Moseley's work, but all that the abstract says of his reference to Bohr's work is, "N. Bohr has faced the difficulty by bringing the idea of the quantum in a novel way. At all events, there is something going on in the atom which is inexplicable by the older mechanics." Moseley explained in a simple manner his classification of the elements by their X-ray spectra. Professor W. M. Hicks, whose contribution to the discussion takes up in the abstracted account nearly three times the space devoted to Rutherford's opening address, was very critical of Bohr. He admitted that the calculation of the exact value of a spectroscopic constant (Rydberg's constant) "has certainly caught the scientific imagination, and one feels convinced, especially on a first reading of his paper, that there is some truth at the bottom of his theory. But . . ." and he goes on to criticize the work in a somewhat futile way. Hicks was an aging man who had devoted most of his life to spectroscopy, having invented a unit of his own, which he called the "oun." Few believed in it at the time and today nobody has heard of it. Very naturally, he did not like to think that his life's work had been rendered nugatory by a young Dane.

RUTHERFORD'S WORK DURING WORLD WAR I

The outbreak of war naturally caused some anxiety, but few thought it was to last for four years and more. The Rutherfords, for his wife had accompanied him, went from Australia to the land of their birth, New Zealand, where they visited friends and relations, including, of course, his parents. At Christchurch, where he had carried out his first research, he received a civic welcome and was, in general, made much of, as was only to be expected. From New Zealand they returned slowly to England by way of Vancouver, Montreal, and New York, seeing many old friends. Boltwood, for instance, came to see them at New York. They did not reach Manchester until early in January 1915. Traveling across the world was a more leisurely business before flying came into the question.

Naturally everything at Manchester had changed. Shortly after his return Rutherford wrote to Schuster, "I do not know if you have heard of the changes the war has made in my Department. Pring has got a Commission as 1st Lieutenant in the Royal Fusiliers, Florance, Andrade, and Walmsley in the Artillery, while

Robinson expects a Commission at any time. . . . Possibly also you have heard that Marsden has been appointed Professor of Physics in Victoria College, Wellington, in succession to Laby, who gained the post in Melbourne. He is leaving here in a week's time to take up his duties." Wellington, the capital of New Zealand, is in the North Island, some two hundred miles from Christchurch in the South Island. In this letter to Schuster, Rutherford said that they would be able "to carry on the work temporarily all right," which sounds as if he, like many others, was anticipating a short war. Before many months had passed, however, he became closely engaged on problems connected with the war, particularly with the task of detecting submarines by the sounds which they made. The basement laboratory at Manchester was used to accommodate a large tank, in which devices for detecting sound carried by water were tested. He wrote to his mother in August 1915, a year after the outbreak of war, that he was on a committee for dealing with submarine problems and in December of the same year saying that he had spent three days in a fishing vessel carrying out experiments. He also served on a Board of Inventions and Research, dealing, as the name suggests, with inventions supposed to have a bearing on the conduct of the war. W. H. Bragg, who was particularly engaged in the practical testing of antisubmarine devices, was in close touch with Rutherford.

In the middle of 1917 Rutherford went to France to discuss his antisubmarine work with his French colleagues, very distinguished physicists, and after that he went to Washington with them, as one of an English and French mission, to talk things over with American colleagues, the United States having entered the war in April. He worked very hard, and wrote to his wife in

June, "The weather is getting pretty warm but I sleep
well in pyjamas without a sheet and generally my constitution stands well the strain of so many lunches and
dinners." Food in England at that time was already
getting short. He traveled extensively in the States, incidentally collecting honorary degrees at Harvard and
Yale. Afterward, naturally, he went to Montreal, the
scene of his early triumph in radioactivity, and saw his
old friends.

On his return to England he found that, although he
still had to serve on various committees, the calls on
his time for such things as antisubmarine investigations
were less severe and he was able to return to his beloved
investigations in the Manchester laboratory, where for
assistance he had mainly to rely upon the stalwart
laboratory steward, Kay. It is an indication of how little time until then, July 1917, he had been able to devote to research, that between 1915 and 1919 he published only two short papers describing new results,
one in conjunction with A. B. Wood, who had made
important contributions to the antisubmarine work. He
had, however, found it possible to participate in scientific meetings, for instance that of the British Ass which
took place in Manchester in 1915, and to give certain
lectures. One of these, delivered in 1916, on "Radiations from Radium," contains a striking passage. Having pointed out that scientists wanted to find how they
could release at will the intrinsic energy contained in
radium, which would mean that from one pound of
material one could obtain as much energy as from a
hundred million pounds of coal, he remarked that up to
the time in question no one had found out how to do
this and personally he was very hopeful that we should
not do so until man was living at peace with his neighbors, which seems to show that at the time he had some

inkling of an atomic bomb. On the whole his work directly concerned with the war, although it could not fail to be of use, was not marked by anything outstanding. He was not, of course, in a position of power, but was subordinate to the naval and military authorities.

The war came to an end with the Armistice of November 11, 1918. It is of some interest, in the view of subsequent history, to quote from a letter which Bohr wrote to Rutherford from Denmark at the time. "All here are convinced that there can never more be a war in Europe of such dimensions; all the people have learnt so much from this dreadful lesson, and even here in these small Scandinavian countries, where, for good reason, there certainly was not much aggressive military spirit before the war, people have got to look quite differently than before at the military side of life. From all that we hear, we feel also quite sure that the men now in power in Germany take a real peaceful attitude, not for the occasion and not because they have always done so, but because all liberal-minded people in the world seem to have understood the unsoundness of the principles on which international politics has hitherto been carried on. If therefore only there will not become anarchy in Germany due to the great need and poverty at the present moment, this time may certainly be looked upon as the beginning of a new era in history."

THE FIRST ARTIFICIAL DISINTEGRATION OF A NUCLEUS

With the end of the war Rutherford was able to devote something like his full energy to the problems which he had in hand. On September 8, 1917, he had begun a new notebook, which he inscribed "Range of High-Speed Atoms in Air and Other Gases." It has been mentioned that Marsden, before his departure for New Zealand, had shown that the passage of alpha rays through hydrogen gave rise to particles which, as evidenced by scintillations, went far beyond the range of the alpha particles themselves, and were attributed to hydrogen nuclei which, struck by the heavier alphas, had a greater velocity. The range calculated on this assumption agreed with experiment. Rutherford busied himself in detail with the effects arising from the passage of alpha particles through gases and in 1919 published his results. Needless to say, he had found much of importance, such as that far more hydrogen nuclei were thrown forward at high speed than were to be anticipated from a simple collision between ordinary particles, from which he drew interesting conclusions as to the forces between nuclear particles at very close approach. However, the result of prime importance arose from the experiments with nitrogen.

The nitrogen nucleus is considerably heavier than the alpha particle, and so should not be driven forward much as the result of being struck. Nevertheless, Rutherford found that when alphas passed through nitrogen, many long-range particles were produced, as they were when the particles passed through hydrogen. With oxygen, the mass of which does not differ much from that of nitrogen, no long-range particles occurred. He further showed, by the use of a magnetic field, that the long-range particles from nitrogen behave like hydrogen nuclei. After several careful checks, he was driven to the conclusion, at that time astonishing, that the nitrogen nucleus had been disintegrated by the impact of the alpha particle, and a hydrogen nucleus knocked out of it. To use his own simple words, "It is difficult to avoid the conclusion that the long-range atoms arising from the collision of alpha particles with nitrogen are not nitrogen atoms but probably atoms of hydrogen, or atoms of mass 2. If this be the case we must conclude that the nitrogen atom is disintegrated under the intense forces developed in a close collision with a swift alpha-particle, and that the hydrogen atom which is liberated formed a constituent part of the nitrogen nucleus." This was a historic statement, announcing the first case of artificial disintegration of a nucleus, which is today such a commonplace. It was the beginning of a new field of research for Rutherford and his school.

ELECTION TO THE CAVENDISH CHAIR OF PHYSICS

It was also his last research at Manchester, a fitting end to a great period. Early in 1919 J. J. Thomson was appointed to be Master of Trinity College, Cambridge, and decided to resign the Cavendish professorship of physics. There was little doubt as to the man best fitted to follow him as head of the Cavendish Laboratory, and on April 2 Rutherford was duly appointed to be the successor of Clerk Maxwell, Lord Rayleigh, and J. J. Thomson, three of the greatest figures in the history of physics. It was not easy for him to leave Manchester. He wrote to his mother on April 7, 1919, "You will have received the news that I have been elected to the Cavendish Chair of Physics held by Sir J. J. Thomson, who is now Master of Trinity. It was a difficult question to decide whether to leave Manchester as they have been very good to me, but I felt it probably best for me to come here, for after all it is the chief physics chair in the country and has turned out most of the physics professors of the last 20 years. I was appointed on April 2 and technically take up office from that date, but as I must finish out the term's work in Manchester, Sir J.J. will be in charge and he is very pleased to do this for me. It will of course be a wrench pulling up my roots again and starting afresh to make new friends, but fortunately I know a good few people there already and will not be a stranger in Trinity College. The latter will no doubt offer me a Fellowship which will give me the rights of the College to dine there when I please." Sure enough, some days later he received from J. J. Thomson the information that he had been unanimously elected a Fellow.

Rutherford duly stayed on at Manchester until the end of the summer term. The university sent him a warm letter of farewell and of congratulation on the distinction of his new post. In his cordial and intimate reply Rutherford said, "I have passed a very happy and fruitful twelve years in your midst and I am sure no one could have been treated with more kindness and consideration than has been shown by all my colleagues. . . . While I am leaving many close friends behind me, I hope that my departure from Manchester will not lead to a complete severance of my ties with the university." It is generally agreed by those who knew him and have written on the point that the happiest years of his life were spent at Manchester, years which saw the birth of the nuclear atom and the first disruption of the nucleus.

Chapter VI

CAMBRIDGE

Rutherford was a very shrewd man. He saw that
there was a danger that J. J. Thomson, so long the
absolute ruler of the Cavendish Laboratory, might be
reluctant to abstain from all share in control of it, in
particular to retire from any participation in the direction of research. With his usual frankness he wrote to
J.J. in March 1919 concerning the Cavendish professorship: "Suppose I stood and were elected I feel that no
advantage of the post could possibly compensate for
any future disturbance of our long continued friendship
or for any possible friction, whether open or latent,
that might possibly arise if we did not have a clear
mutual understanding with regard to the laboratory and
research arrangements." The reply that he received was
reassuring, containing the words, "I am very glad to
find that you are still entertaining the possibility of coming to Cambridge as Professor. If you do, you will find
that I shall leave you an absolutely free hand in the
management of the Laboratory." J.J. strictly carried
out this undertaking. He was appointed professor of
physics, without stipend, and private rooms with facilities for research were allotted to him. As Master of
Trinity College, holder of the most important academic
post in Cambridge, he occupied a suite of beautiful
rooms in the college and was generously remunerated,
so that the lack of professorial stipend was in no sense

a hardship. The appointment was in the nature of a tribute to his wonderful work as head of the Cavendish Laboratory. He continued to do a certain amount of experimental research, and he gave notable lectures, including a course on "The Electron in Chemistry," at the Franklin Institute of Philadelphia in 1923, subsequently published as a book.

Rutherford was, naturally, most warmly welcomed at Cambridge, where he had many friends. As already mentioned, he had been elected a Fellow of Trinity College. Dining there at the High Table, as the long table reserved for Fellows and their guests is called, he came to know well many men of the greatest distinction in subjects other than science, such as A. E. Housman, Regius professor of Latin and a lyric poet of exceptional qualities, whose book of early poems, *A Shropshire Lad,* is famous. Rutherford and his wife found an old-fashioned two-story house, standing in a large garden with a fine lawn under spreading trees. It was called Newnham Cottage, although larger than is usually implied by the word cottage. Here he lived until his death.

If Rutherford's early days at Cambridge were characterized by outstanding research on the ionization of gases, his years at McGill by the establishment of the fundamental laws of radioactivity, and the Manchester period by the discovery of the nuclear atom, then the years as head of the Cavendish Laboratory may be said to be marked by the disruption of the nucleus. Although he personally achieved great things, he was, perhaps, able to take less direct part in the research of his school than he had done at Manchester, and some of the fundamental discoveries made under his sway and influence do not bear his name.

He brought with him from Manchester much of his

apparatus for research on problems of radioactivity, which, simple as it was, would have taken time to produce and test at Cambridge. He also brought his very necessary supply of radium. He would have liked to bring his invaluable laboratory steward, who had a deep affection and admiration for him, but Kay decided for family reasons to stay in Manchester. Rutherford was at once joined in Cambridge by James Chadwick, who had graduated at Manchester and there carried out research on radioactive problems from 1911 until 1913, when he had gone to work with Geiger in Germany. He was caught in Germany by the outbreak of war in 1914 and was interned at Ruhleben as a civilian prisoner-of-war for the duration. Chadwick was destined to do research of prime importance at Cambridge and was awarded the Nobel Prize in 1935 for the discovery of the neutron, which plays so large a part in nuclear physics. Interned with Chadwick was C. D. Ellis, who, about to become a regular officer in the British artillery, happened to be taking a holiday in Germany in the summer of 1914. This is mentioned because during the long prison-camp association with Chadwick he acquired an enthusiasm for physics. He came to Cambridge after the war and carried out under Rutherford important research on the beta and gamma rays.

A Song to Celebrate Rutherford's Appointment

Every year there was held in Cambridge a Cavendish dinner, attended by all the workers in the laboratory, a custom which had been inaugurated in 1897, in J. J. Thomson's days. After the dinner it was the practice to sing songs, many of which had been specially written for the occasion by A. A. Robb, F.R.S., at one time a worker in the laboratory. The following is one which he composed to celebrate Rutherford's appointment. It was sung to the tune of "I Love a Lassie," at the time a very popular song; to get the full effect the reader must imagine the chorus sung by a roomful of young men who had dined well and were all full of enthusiasm for the new chief and all in full voice, if not always in full tune. It was called "Induced Activity."

> We've a professor
> A jolly smart professor,
> Who's director of the lab. in Free School Lane.
> He's quite an acquisition
> To the cause of erudition,
> As I hope very briefly to explain.
> When first he did arrive here
> He made everything alive here,
> For, said he, "the place will never do at all;
> I'll make it nice and tidy,
> And I'll hire a Cambridge *lidy*
> Just to sweep down the cobwebs from the wall."

> *Chorus*

> He's the successor
> Of his great predecessor,
> And their wondrous deeds can never be ignored:
> Since they're birds of a feather,
> We link them both together,
> J.J. and Rutherford.

> Said he, "I wonder
> How, in the name of thunder,
> All this rubbish has accumulated here,
> Since Maxwell and since Rayleigh
> It has been a-gathering daily,
> That's a thing that is manifest and clear."
> And so he spoke to Lincoln,

And, said he, "I have been thinkin'
That the lab. is not as neat as it might be;
You understand my meaning,
That it needs a darned good cleaning,
As I think Mr. Lincoln you'll agree."

    Chorus: He's the successor, etc.

Such is the story
Of how the laboratory
Came to look again so tidy and so bright;
The Prof. was so elated
When he saw it renovated
He at once started whistling with delight.
So great was the temptation
To begin investigation
That he started his researches there and then,
And what he's been achieving
Would be almost past believing
If he weren't quite a marvel among men.

    Chorus: He's the successor, etc.

What's in an atom,
The innermost substratum?
That's the problem he is working at today.
He lately did discover
How to shoot them down like plover,
And the poor little things can't get away.
He uses as munitions
On his hunting expeditions
Alpha particles which out of Radium spring.
It's really most surprising,
And it needed some devising,
How to shoot down an atom on the wing.

    Chorus: He's the successor, etc.

It should be noted that Lincoln was the head of the Cavendish workshop. This song will indicate clearly how Rutherford had the place cleaned up as a start.

NUCLEAR DISRUPTION

As soon as things had settled down in the laboratory, Rutherford started again on the sensational work which he was pursuing in his last days at Manchester, the disintegration of the nuclei of light elements by the impact of alpha particles. The apparatus was still, in those days, of the simplest construction. In the case of a gas, such as nitrogen, the alpha rays from a radioactive source, a little plate coated with radium (B + C), passed through the gas contained in a tube, and the particles produced passed out through a hole covered by a thin foil, whose stopping power was that of only two or three inches of air. The particles were observed with the aid of a little phosphorescent zinc sulphide screen, the scintillations produced in which were viewed with the usual low-power microscope. In the case of a solid, such as aluminum, the tube was evacuated and the foil that constituted the window was made of the metal in question. Thin absorbing screens could be placed between the metal window and the zinc sulphide in order to measure the penetrating power, or range, of the particles produced by the disruption.

Rutherford soon showed conclusively, from their behavior in a magnetic field, that the particles which the alphas knocked out of the nitrogen were in fact, as he had conjectured, hydrogen nuclei. About this time Rutherford thought that the nucleus of the hydrogen atoms, which plays so prominent a part in general nuclear physics, should have a special name and he suggested that it be called the *proton,* a designation that was at once adopted. From now on it will be so called. An ordinary hydrogen atom, then, is a proton loosely associated with one electron.

With Chadwick he then proceeded, with the simple apparatus just described, to a systematic investigation of the disintegration of other light elements. It was soon found that the particles produced by the disruption were emitted more or less equally in all directions, and the apparatus was then modified to count the particles sent out by the struck element in a direction at right angles to that of the bombarding alpha rays, a method which had certain advantages.

The general result of this work was that definite evidence of nuclear disruption was obtained for twelve light elements. In each case a swift proton was driven out, which meant that the nucleus must lose one unit of positive charge and so change its chemical nature. The fate of the swift alpha particle involved in the collision that resulted in the liberation of the proton was not at first known, but if it was captured the nuclear charge would clearly be increased by one unit. It was soon shown that in the case of nitrogen such a capture did take place; the nitrogen atom, nuclear charge 7, became an oxygen atom, nuclear charge 8, but with mass one unit greater than that of the ordinary oxygen atom, that is, it became an isotope of oxygen.

Whether the active alpha were captured or not, it was clear that what had been done was to change the chemical nature of the element whose nucleus had been broken. The work of Rutherford and Soddy, in the Canadian days, had shown that radioactive atoms spontaneously changed their chemical nature, in a way that could not be influenced by heat, chemical reaction, or any other laboratory method. What had now been shown was that, by the use of the energetic little alpha particle, the nature of ordinary nonradioactive atoms could be changed. Not, of course, very many of them, not enough to approach, even distantly, a weighable quantity: only about one alpha particle in a million was effective in producing a transmutation, and the total number of alphas used in one experiment would not make up a weighable quantity. But the principle was proved: the chemical nature of an ordinary stable element could be changed by laboratory methods.

ATOMIC TRANSMUTATION

From ancient times there had been a belief in the possibility of transmuting common metals—base metals, as they were called—into noble metals, gold and silver, a matter with which the medieval study of alchemy was much concerned. In the Middle Ages this belief was widespread. One of Chaucer's tales, written nearly six hundred years ago, is concerned with a swindler who professed to be able to turn copper into silver, and, with the aid of a furnace and silver filings hidden in wax, persuaded his victim that he had done so. Later, many men spent their lives in the pursuit of such endeavor, in particular in the search for the "Philosopher's Stone," which was supposed to have mystic powers, including that of transmuting metals. Some of these men were serious students of such science as existed in their day; others were charlatans. Ben Jonson's play *The Alchemist,* 1610, deals with one of the latter. However, from the time of the foundation of modern chemistry, which may be said to have begun with the work of Robert Boyle in the second half of the seventeenth century, belief in the impossibility of changing one element into another became more and more firmly established, and a quotation from the great and far-seeing Clerk Maxwell has already been given, expressing his conviction that atoms were, and always had been, in all circumstances unchangeable. But now came Rutherford, who showed that, on the contrary, certain atomic transmutations could be provoked at will, although the quantities involved were exceedingly small. With the old beliefs in mind Rutherford wrote in 1937, the last year of his life, a little book called *The Newer Alchemy,* describing in popular fashion the work of his laboratory on this amazing subject.

While in a sense these experiments of Rutherford's, alone and in collaboration with Chadwick, may be said to have been the beginning of a new era, an era in which untold millions of dollars were to be spent on atomic transmutations, with results that put the existence of the human race in danger, on the other hand in another sense they were the end of an old era. In Plate VIII Rutherford is shown holding lightly in his hands the insignificant apparatus with which the first fundamental transmutation results were obtained. This represents the old, typically Rutherfordian, method of going to work. The age initiated by John D. (later Sir John) Cockcroft and E. T. S. Walton's experiments in the Cavendish Laboratory, to be described later, was about to set in, when constructions on an electrical-engineering scale were to be employed for work on the transmutation of the elements. This nuclear engineering, as it is called today, has proceeded to extraordinary lengths. Today, for instance, the great international apparatus for nuclear transmutation erected at Geneva covers about ten acres.

A PROPHETIC BAKERIAN LECTURE

In 1920 Rutherford was appointed by the Royal Society to give the Bakerian lecture for the second time, a very rare distinction. His first Bakerian lecture in 1904, referred to in Chapter IV, was noteworthy as an exposition of the newly born science of radioactivity, long before the nucleus had been discovered and shown to be the seat of radioactive change. He was then a young man, thirty-two years of age, who had been recently made a Fellow of the Royal Society. In this second lecture, given at the age of forty-seven, when he was world-famous, he dealt not with the spontaneous atomic changes of his first lecture, but with the provoked transmutations demonstrated in the work which has just been described. The lecture is remarkable not only as a convincing exposition of the results of these experiments, but also for some astonishing predictions. He stated that it seemed very likely that a nucleus could exist having a mass of two units and a charge of one unit, which would, of course, with its electron behave chemically like hydrogen, or, in other words, would be an isotope of hydrogen. This "heavy hydrogen," to be called deuterium, was discovered eleven years later in America by Harold C. Urey, Ferdinand G. Brickwedde, and George M. Murphy. Rutherford also anticipated the existence of a particle with a mass of three units and a charge of two units, namely a lighter isotope of helium, likewise to be discovered later. But most remarkable of all was his anticipation of the existence of a particle with zero nuclear charge, the neutron, to be discovered twelve years later by Chadwick in the Cavendish Laboratory. The neutron is perhaps the most important particle in modern atomic physics; at any rate it plays a leading part in today's large-scale nuclear transmutations.

To show how definite and how clear were these predictions of Rutherford's, his actual words may well be quoted: "If we are correct in this assumption it seems very likely that one electron can also bind two hydrogen nuclei and possibly also one hydrogen nucleus. In the one case, this entails the possible existence of an atom of mass nearly 2 carrying one charge, which is to be regarded as an isotope of hydrogen. In the other case, it involves the idea of the possible existence of an atom of mass 1 which has zero nuclear charge. Such an atomic structure seems by no means impossible. On present views, the neutral hydrogen atom is regarded as a nucleus of unit charge with an electron attached at a distance, and the spectrum of hydrogen is ascribed to the movement of this distant electron. Under some conditions, however, it may be possible for an electron to combine much more closely with the hydrogen nucleus, forming a kind of neutral doublet. Such an atom would have very novel properties. Its external field would be practically zero, except very close to the nucleus, and in consequence it should be able to move freely through matter. Its presence would probably be difficult to detect by the spectroscope, and it may be impossible to contain it in a sealed vessel. On the other hand, it should enter readily the structure of atoms, and may either unite with the nucleus or be disintegrated by its intense field, resulting possibly in the escape of a charged hydrogen atom or an electron or both.

"The existence of such atoms seems almost necessary to explain the building up of the nuclei of heavy elements; for unless we suppose the production of charged particles of very high velocities it is difficult to see how any positively charged particle can reach the nucleus of a heavy atom against its intense repulsive field."

This penetrating power, this reaction with the nucleus, are outstanding properties of the neutron.

A few people realized at once the far-reaching significance of this lecture. Strange to say, one of the first and most enthusiastic appreciations came from the famous biologist Jacques Loeb, a German who had settled in the United States and was on friendly terms with Rutherford. He wrote as soon as the lecture was published: "The most wonderful part is that it looks as if you were just entering on a new series of scientific conquests," and later in the same letter, after referring to the growing hold of bureaucracy on scientific research, "I am under the impression that your Bakerian lecture will do more for science than all the National Research Councils in the world put together,"[1] which may appear to some to be a very old-fashioned sentiment.

CHADWICK AND THE DISCOVERY OF THE NEUTRON

Let us skip eleven years and consider how the existence of the neutron came to be proved in the Cavendish. It was the examination of radiation produced by bombarding the element beryllium with alpha particles, the process that Rutherford had shown to be so fruitful, that led to its discovery. Beryllium is a very light metal—much lighter than aluminum—which has the atomic number 4 and atomic weight 9, that is, 4 times the charge and 9 times the mass of the hydrogen nucleus. It was first prepared, and derives its name, from the mineral beryl, one variety of which is the gem stone known by that name, while other varieties are

[1] Quoted by Norman Feather, *Lord Rutherford,* pp. 163, 164.

the aquamarine and the emerald, dear to ladies. Strangely enough, the element is also called glucinum from a Greek word meaning "sweet," because of the sweet taste of its salts! F. Joliot and his wife, Irène Joliot-Curie, who was Marie Curie's daughter, had found in 1931 that this radiation from beryllium had peculiar properties: for instance, it was very penetrating and its ionizing effect was increased by putting materials containing hydrogen, of which paraffin wax is a convenient example often used in physical research, between the beryllium and the chamber used for measuring the ionization. These properties they explained by assuming that the radiation sent out by the bombarded beryllium could knock protons out of the wax—but how?

Chadwick, who was at the time assistant director of research and had been so closely associated with Rutherford in disintegrating light atoms, turned his attention to trying to solve this problem. He proceeded in a typically simple Rutherfordian way, using a radium F (polonium) coating on a disc as his source of alpha rays: this source has the great advantage that there are no accompanying beta and gamma rays, which would have a disturbing effect. In front of this source was placed a disc of pure beryllium, which thus became the source of the unknown radiation. To detect the mysterious rays he used an ionization chamber, connected with a valve amplifier which worked a recorder registering on photographic paper. Every time a particle producing ionization entered the chamber its arrival was registered photographically on a moving strip of paper. By this time the old scintillation method of counting had quite gone out and a self-registering valve device, of one kind or another, had taken its place, which was, needless to say, a great improvement.

The experiments were straightforward. Chadwick found that putting a slab of metal, even an inch of lead, between the beryllium and the counting chamber made no difference to the number of counts per minute, which showed that the radiation was very penetrating. Putting a slab of paraffin wax in the path of the beryllium rays very much increased the count, showing that ionizing particles were knocked out of the wax. By means of absorbing screens the greatest range of these ionizing particles was measured and found to be equivalent to sixteen inches of air. By comparison of the ionizing power of these particles with the ionization produced by protons of this range (that is, of the same speed) it was conclusively shown that these particles struck out of paraffin wax were protons. The final step was to show that these protons expelled from the wax behaved just as if they had been propelled by bombardment with particles of the same mass as a proton. But the only way in which the ability of a particle of the mass of a proton to pass through an inch of lead could be explained was to assume that it had no charge, for, as Rutherford had pointed out, an uncharged particle could pass very close to a charged nucleus or an electron without any effect. Thus, in 1932, the existence of the neutron was established. Direct collision of a neutron with a nucleus, of the kind that produces the expelled protons, is a very rare event. It could be observed, as in Chadwick's experiments, because there was such an enormous number of neutrons coming from the beryllium.

Chadwick, of course, was very familiar with Rutherford's prediction of the existence of the neutron and of its properties. Joliot stated that if he and his wife had read the Bakerian lecture in which this prediction was made it was distinctly possible that they would have anticipated Chadwick in identifying the nature of their mysterious radiation, but they explained that, although they studied with care all original publications in their field of research, they did not read such lectures because it was rare to find in them anything that had not been published elsewhere. Apparently they did not know Rutherford's way as well as they should have done.

THE WILSON CLOUD CHAMBER

Before passing on to deal with other great discoveries made in the Cavendish under Rutherford's rule, something must be said of a marvelous process, extensively used in the researches in question, which makes visible the paths of single alpha particles and of other swift particles producing ions in gases. This method was devised by C. T. R. Wilson and the apparatus used is known as the Wilson cloud chamber. By a simple device minute drops of water, so small that they cannot be seen singly and do not fall through the air appreciably in a matter of seconds, are made to condense on the ions, thus forming a white line which clearly reveals the track of the ionizing particle and can be photographed, as can be seen in Plates IX and XII.

The young Wilson was originally brought to the idea on which his method depends by watching with admiration from the summit of Ben Nevis, the highest mountain in Scotland, the glories of the surrounding clouds and conceiving the wish to make clouds in the laboratory. He was then twenty-five years old, being two years older than Rutherford; they were soon to come together in the Cavendish Laboratory, for it was there that C.T.R., as he was affectionately called, proceeded to make artificial clouds with a small glass vessel in which air was suddenly expanded by a controlled amount. A given space can hold a certain amount of water as vapor without its condensing to drops, the amount which can be so held being greater the higher the temperature. It is a familiar fact that the water vapor always present in a warm room deposits a coat of liquid water on a cold window pane because the cold air in contact with the glass cannot hold all the vapor that is invisibly present in the warm air.

When air is suddenly expanded it cools, just as air that is compressed becomes warmer, as anyone who has pumped up a tire by hand knows. When C.T.R., then, suddenly expanded his air saturated with water vapor it cooled, and a cloud of very very small water drops was produced, just the kind of minute drops that make up a natural cloud.

The drops which form from a supersaturated vapor—that is, from a vapor comprising more water than the space can normally hold—require some kind of particle on which to condense, just as, in a room crowded with more people than it can comfortably hold, chairs are required if some of them are to sit down in groups, in order to reduce the number of those moving about to a reasonable figure. Such centers of condensation are provided in normal air by minute dust particles that are always present if special steps have not been taken to remove them. However, Wilson found in 1896 that ions—single charged molecules produced by X-rays, for instance—could act as centers of condensation; it is the electric field surrounding them that has the effect. In other words, bottled clouds could be produced by suddenly expanding in small vessels air saturated with water vapor that had been ionized by any means, while the same conditions of expansion did not lead to condensation if the air, previously rendered dust-free, was not ionized.

The dates are mentioned because Wilson was a very careful worker, who proceeded in accordance with Goethe's motto, *ohne Hast, aber ohne Rast,* without haste, but without rest. He did, for instance, all his own glass-blowing and put together superbly well all his own beautifully designed apparatus. Typical of the things that used to be said about him in affectionate jest is Rutherford's remark on his return from a visit to New Zealand in 1925: "But all good things come to an end and we arrived back in the old country and so to Cambridge. The first thing that I did after being away for some months was to look up my old friend C.T.R. I found him still grinding a large glass joint!"

C.T.R. found the exact amount of expansion needed to produce best his minute fogs, and quietly proceeded to perfect each process of which he made use. Finally, in 1911, he showed that the track of an alpha particle could be made visible as a white line, consisting of minute drops condensing on the ions formed by its passage. This he did by the appropriate expansion of moist air in a small cylindrical vessel, closed at the top by a flat glass plate through which the tracks could be seen, and at the bottom by a piston that could be suddenly dropped by an appropriate amount.

In the following year he devised a larger and much improved cloud chamber and produced superb photographs of alpha and beta ray tracks and of the tracks of moving electrons produced by a beam of X-rays. Patrick Blackett, who, as will be shortly described, developed the method with results of first importance, wrote in 1960 that these early ray-track pictures taken by C. T. R. Wilson remain among the technically best photographs of this class ever made. Beautiful examples of photographs taken with the Wilson cloud chamber method are shown in Plates IX and XII.

If some time has been spent in describing this extraordinary achievement, produced with fundamentally simple means, it is because the cloud chamber proved to be one of the most fruitful methods of investigating the machinery of nuclear physics. In the last chapter mention was made of Rutherford's reference, in his speech at Melbourne in 1914, to alpha ray tracks recorded by C. T. R. Wilson's cloud chamber. In the Cavendish Laboratory in Rutherford's time it led to results of supreme importance and it has been used all over the world in atomic research until the present day. The famous bubble chamber employed so much today in high-energy nuclear physics is a direct descendant of C. T. R. Wilson's apparatus, one of the most beautiful devices of modern physics.

PATRICK BLACKETT

We pass to consider Patrick Blackett's work, which made use of the cloud chamber to attain one of the great successes of the Cavendish in those days. It was initiated by Rutherford in 1921, when he was in the midst of his work with Chadwick on the disruption of light nuclei by alpha particles. It naturally occurred to him that what actually took place in the collision might be recorded by the cloud chamber method, which would show the path of the alpha particle before impact and the paths of resultant particles after impact. For this purpose a cloud apparatus for taking a large number of particles was planned, a large number being necessary because a close collision occurs very seldom. A Japanese research man, T. Shimizu, started on the work, but returned to Japan before any results of importance

had been obtained, and to continue it Rutherford chose
Blackett, who had just graduated at the age of twenty-
three, having served in the Navy during the 1914–18
war.

Blackett built a cloud chamber apparatus which automatically took a photograph every fifteen seconds, the
piston going up and down at regular intervals. Two
photographs, viewing from directions at right angles,
were taken of each track, which made it possible to work
out just what happened when two particles resulted
from the collision. One photograph would not give the
angle of the fork, any more than the shadow produced
by a single source of light would give the angle between two fingers held up if the position of the hand
was not known. What Blackett could do, then, was to
find the range and position of each particle produced
by the close impact of an alpha particle—if he had a
photograph of a desired kind of collision!

A large number of photographs taken with different
gases—hydrogen, helium, nitrogen, and argon—showed
an occasional instance of a forked track in which the
two prongs agreed exactly, in length and angle, with
what was to be expected if the alpha particle made an
elastic collision with the struck nucleus, just as if a
billiard ball had struck another similar ball of a different mass. This was not what Blackett was looking
for; he wanted evidence of nuclear disruption.

To find this evidence required, as will be seen, a certain amount of patience, as well as the greatest experimental skill. In a few months in 1924 Blackett took
some 23,000 photographs of alpha ray tracks in nitrogen. There were, on an average, 18 tracks on each
photographic plate, so that he had in all some 400,000
tracks. Among these he found eight branched tracks of
a new character, one branch being a very long thin

track, shown to be due to a proton, and the other a short, thick branch. One of his best photographs is shown in Plate IX, where the long thin track passing to the left in a slightly downward direction is the path of the proton driven out of a nitrogen nucleus. The short thick branch going upward slightly to the right is the track of the oxygen isotope formed by the impact.

That an oxygen isotope results from the impact is clear from the following considerations. If the alpha particle, in intimate collision, had knocked the proton out of the nitrogen nucleus and bounced off again, as it did in collision with, for instance, an oxygen nucleus, then there should have been three resultant tracks, made respectively by the proton, the struck nitrogen nucleus, and the deflected alpha. That there was only one resultant track beside that of the proton showed that the alpha particle must have become one with the nitrogen nucleus. Since the charge on the nitrogen nucleus is 7, the new nucleus formed must have a charge 8, which is that characteristic of the oxygen atom, and a mass of 17 units, whereas ordinary oxygen has a mass of 16 units. The newly formed nucleus must be, then, that of an isotope of oxygen. This isotope was soon after proved to exist by an optical method. Thus with a few single atoms a new type of nuclear transformation, later showed to be common, was conclusively proved. It would require millions of millions of atoms to form an amount weighable in a delicate balance. The new method weighed single atoms.

THE POSITRON

This work of Blackett's was undertaken at Rutherford's direct incentive, in the early years of his rule at the Cavendish, when he was closely concerned with all that was going on. But as we are dealing both with Blackett and the Wilson cloud chamber it may be well to describe here a piece of fundamental work due to the same combination, although it was carried out many years later. Other workers had occasionally detected on cloud chamber photographs tracks not due to intentional laboratory sources: these tracks had been ascribed to the effect of particles coming from outer space. Blackett, with the collaboration of C. P. S. Occhialini, worked out a method of making a cosmic ray particle, as these visitors from outer space are called, set the cloud chamber to work, so that it recorded only when such a particle was passing through it. They effected this by placing a Geiger counter above and a similar counter below the chamber, so that any ray that passed through both counters must also pass through the chamber. By an ingenious arrangement of circuits the simultaneous discharge of the two counters was made to operate the expansion of the chamber: the ions produced by the rays hung about long enough for the slightly later expansion to deposit the usual droplets on them. In this way photographs were taken only when there was something important to record. The chamber was placed in a magnetic field, which, of course, bends the track of a moving charged particle, in one direction if it is positively charged and in the other direction if it is negatively charged.

Blackett and Occhialini found in this way a large number of tracks, some of which were curved in one direction and others curved in the opposite direction. Calculation showed that while those of one direction corresponded to the familiar electron, those of the other direction corresponded to particles of exactly the same mass and of charge of exactly the same size, but of opposite sign. Here was the particle that had often been sought, but until this time never found, the positive electron, or positron, as it is called. Carl D. Anderson had just discovered the positron with a normal cloud chamber in the United States, but here was completely independent confirmation of it. All this was in 1933. In 1948, years after Rutherford's death, Blackett was awarded the Nobel Prize "For his improvement of the Wilson cloud-chamber method and for the resulting discoveries in the field of nuclear physics and cosmic rays."

APPLETON AND RADIO WAVES

Chadwick's discovery of the neutron and Blackett's work with the cloud chamber that led to the positron have been given as examples of how young men, coming to the Cavendish in the early days of Rutherford's rule, just after the First World War, were stimulated by his encouragement and set by him on the path that led to their great discoveries. But just as there had been in his Manchester laboratory men engaged on research outside the field of radioactivity, in whose work he nevertheless took a benevolent interest, so in those days at the Cavendish there were a few nonatomic men of outstanding distinction. Celebrated among these was E. V. Appleton, now Sir Edward, who in 1947 received the Nobel Prize for his work on the physical properties of the upper atmosphere, including his discovery of the layer of electrified air, extending upward from a height of about 125 miles, known as the Appleton layer. During the First World War, as an officer in the Engineers, he became interested in the propagation and fading of radio signals and, when the war was over, like Chadwick and Blackett, he went to Cambridge. Rutherford naturally wanted to put him to work on some aspect of nuclear physics, but Appleton was anxious to work on the subject of radio. He has recorded how he explained his plans to Rutherford, who, when he had finished, said, "Go ahead. I'll back you," which meant diverting some of the none too plentiful research funds from very small particles, his particular buddies, to very long waves, now strangers to him. Perhaps he remembered his early days of research on wireless waves, perhaps he recognized in Appleton a winner.

At any rate, Rutherford took a keen interest in Appleton's work, which in a few years proved the real existence of a layer of ionized air in the upper atmosphere. A. E. Kennelly in the United States and Oliver Heaviside in England had independently assumed the presence of such a layer in order to explain how it was that wireless waves could travel round the world. The sheet of electrified particles acts as a reflector of the long electromagnetic waves. Appleton also discovered a second similar layer higher up, called the Appleton layer, to which reference has just been made. It was with Rutherford's direct encouragement, then, that Appleton carried out his first work on radio waves and the upper atmosphere, and although he left Cambridge in 1924 to take up the professorship of physics at King's College, London, while holding which post he carried out some of his most important work, Rutherford always maintained the friendliest relations with him. It is typical that Appleton, in his speech at the formal banquet at Stockholm on the occasion of the award of the Nobel prizes, said, "Perhaps you will understand me when I say that I much regret that my old professor, Lord Rutherford, a Nobel Prizeman himself, who gave me the warmest encouragement and help when I began to work on the ionosphere, is not alive today to let me hear his own words of approval." On another occasion Appleton said, very truly, that Rutherford was as remarkable for what he inspired other people to do as for what he did himself. This applies particularly to the period now being considered.

PROJECTS AT THE CAVENDISH

A great man working in the Cavendish in those days, but quite independently of Rutherford, was F. W. Aston, whose work on isotopes was fundamental for atomic physics. He had begun this work, and first made his name, under J. J. Thomson and continued it after the war, always in the Cavendish Laboratory. He was a solitary worker, who achieved astonishing results with apparatus of fundamentally simple design, and his findings were of great importance for mass considerations in the transmutation of light nuclei, as will be mentioned later. He was a close friend of Rutherford's, who, as G. Hevesy has written, was the man whom he admired more than anyone else. He used to play golf regularly with Rutherford and others, the party being known as the "talking foursome." A record of some of the talk would be interesting! Aston was another of the Cavendish Nobel Prize winners, having been chosen for the award in 1922, in the same year that Niels Bohr received it for physics. Like Rutherford, Aston received the prize for chemistry, not physics!

Another famous man working in the Cavendish, his room being actually next to Rutherford's, was Geoffrey Taylor, who was concerned with problems of what is known as classical physics, that is, physics as it was before the coming of X-rays, the electron, and radioactivity. He was doing fundamental work on such matters as the turbulence of the atmosphere, particularly difficult cases of the motion of liquids and certain mechanical properties of metals, matters so remote from

Rutherford's interests that he once said, "I can't understand how anyone as intelligent as Geoffrey Taylor can work on that stuff." He was, however, one of Rutherford's great friends and a member of the talking foursome, of which he said, much later, "Both Rutherford and I were bad golfers and I must confess it was mainly for the pleasure of listening to Rutherford that I played at all." Another member of the foursome was Rutherford's son-in-law, R. H. Fowler, an outstanding theoretical physicist who was also a great Cavendish figure. Years after Rutherford's death Geoffrey Taylor was destined to be concerned in the work on the atomic bomb at Los Alamos, in connection with the destructive effects to be expected from the blast of a huge explosion of the type contemplated, so that his work and Rutherford's were to come together, in a way that neither of them could in the least have foreseen in those days.

In the period 1920 to 1930, the first ten years of Rutherford's sway, the Cavendish Laboratory was a very lively place, full, in the early days, of young men back from the war or from the disruptions of wartime conditions, anxious to work with an enthusiasm that matched that of their chief. Rutherford himself was, of course, absorbed on the one hand with directing their research, with the usual fruitful chats and suggestions, and on the other hand with his own personal pursuits—not that the two activities could be sharply separated. There were first of all the fundamental experiments on nuclear transmutations, already described, all carried out with the old scintillation method, which at the end of the period was to pass out in favor of automatic recordings of the arrival of energetic particles. There was extensive use of the Wilson cloud chamber to examine nuclear collisions and their effects, as exemplified by the work of Blackett. There was also a series of researches by Rutherford, Chadwick, E. S. Bieler, and others concerned with the size of the nucleus and with the electric field close to it, in a way an extension of the original Geiger-Marsden experiments on the scattering of alpha particles. The alpha particle was used as the probe and the old scintillation method to detect the path of the scattered particles. The very small radius of the heavy nuclei was confirmed and the fact that the inverse-square law of force held accurately up to the nuclear region. The results will not be detailed, for they did not lead to anything particularly significant. It was really too early to solve problems of nuclear structure. The neutron, which forms an essential component of the nucleus, had not yet been discovered, and certain very important theories of the interaction of nuclear particles had not yet been put forward.

Important work was also done on the beta and gamma radiations, with which many well-known names were concerned. Much of this applied to the electron structure of the atom and the energy levels in it first postulated by Bohr, the study of which my old Heidelberg friend Walther Kossel had done much to extend and clarify. It is hoped that these few words may suggest the buzzing hive of activity that the Cavendish was.

HONORS AND FAME

During the period 1920 to 1930 Rutherford's name and fame became even more widely known than in the Manchester days and the honors bestowed on him were accompanied by greater and greater demands upon his time for public functions and special lectures. In 1923, for instance, he was president of the British Association, at meetings of which he had, in his younger days, often popularized, discussed and defended his discoveries. He gave a vigorous address at the Association meeting at Liverpool on the electrical structure of matter, which was broadcast throughout the British Isles, the first time that such an address had been made public in such a way. The next year the Association had its annual meeting at Toronto, and Rutherford traveled thither, with his wife, to speak on atomic disintegration. Needless to say, he used the opportunity for informal visits to old Canadian friends and other such recreation, after which he gave a series of lectures at American universities, lectures much attended by senior students on whom his boisterous enthusiasm for his subject had an animating effect. After this he returned to Canada and gave a lecture at his old haunt, McGill, in Montreal, on the disintegration of the radio elements. It need hardly be said that in the same year he lectured also in England outside Cambridge—for instance at the Royal Institution, on the nucleus of the atom. All this should serve to indicate something of his many activities outside the laboratory.

At the beginning of the next year, 1925, he received an outstanding official recognition of his status in the scientific world and in public life, the award of the Order of Merit. This is a British honor of the highest distinction: the number of members of the Order is limited to twenty-four, including national figures in the army and navy. It is customarily conferred on the President of the Royal Society, but Rutherford had not yet held that office. Incidentally, Winston Churchill is a member of the Order and in 1945 Dwight D. Eisenhower was made an honorary member.

At the end of the same year Rutherford was duly elected President of the Royal Society, an office which is habitually held for five years, alternately by a representative of the physical sciences and of the biological sciences. Thus Rutherford succeeded Charles Sherrington, whose work on the nervous system started a new epoch in that subject, and was succeeded by Gowland Hopkins, the discoverer of the significance of vitamins. Rutherford made no attempt to hide his delight at the election to an office to which he devoted great attention. He proved an excellent president in every way, showing in the chair a typically lively interest in whatever was going on. H. E. Armstrong, a man of a very critical nature, who had been a Fellow of the society for nearly fifty years, wrote to him: "Your attitude in the Chair is delightful; to have a President asking questions and prompting discussion is an astounding departure." Characteristic of Rutherford's chairmanship is an anecdote which Professor R. W. James, who did important work on crystal structures, tells of the occasion in 1927 when, as a young man, he read a paper at the Royal Society. Before the formal meeting began Rutherford took him by the arm and said, "You haven't read a paper here before, have you? Do you mind if I give you some advice?" Naturally James said that he would be very grateful, whereupon Rutherford, pointing to the great presidential chair, replied, "Well, for Heaven's sake don't be too difficult. If you knew what I have to put up with, sitting in that chair!" In this way he put the young man at his ease.

Just before he became President of the Royal Society, Rutherford made a lengthy tour in Australia and New Zealand, being away about five months. As usual, he gave a number of lectures. His visit to his homeland, New Zealand, was, naturally, the occasion of great celebrations and crowded lecture halls—at an address in Auckland, in the northern island, there were five hundred standing and five hundred who could not get in at all. Rutherford immensely enjoyed these duties and visits, but naturally they took him much away from the laboratory. The tour in New Zealand was a particularly lengthy break, but a few years later the annual meeting of the British Association took place in South Africa and Rutherford made this the occasion of another tour, lasting some months. Of course in those days there were no long-distance flying services and the sea voyages to such places took much time. Naturally in South Africa there were laboratories to be opened and lectures to be given, as well as mountains and forests to be seen. Rutherford loved these visits to wild scenes, which possibly reminded him of his early days. Duty and pleasure also took him to haunts of old civilization, such as Como, in Italy, the birthplace of the great discoverer Alessandro Volta, after whom the volt is named. The centenary of his birth was celebrated there in 1927, and Rutherford duly gave an address. To these distractions must be added the lectures on the occasions of medals and honors received and of the opening of laboratories and suchlike.

The honors culminated at the end of 1930 with the award, in what are termed the New Year's Honours since they are announced on New Year's Day, of a peerage. Rutherford was created "Baron Rutherford of Nelson," which means that he was called Lord Rutherford. It has already been told how he chose to be "of Nelson" in honor of his native land. His father died at the age of eighty-nine in 1928, but his mother was still alive at the age of eighty-seven and to her he sent a loving telegram: "Now Lord Rutherford more your honour than mine. Ernest." His mother was to die in 1935 at the age of ninety-two, only two years before the man himself.

About a week before the award of the peerage Rutherford suffered a great blow. His daughter Eileen, married to R. H. Fowler, died shortly after the birth of her fourth child. She was his only child and very dear to him: the loss perceptibly aged him. His grandchildren remained his great delight to the end.

PROFESSOR KAPITZA

Before we pass on to the 1930s, reference must be made to an event which did much to lead to a new type of activity in the Cavendish. This was the arrival in 1921 of a Russian, Peter Kapitza, who was destined to remain with Rutherford until 1934 and to have much influence on him.

Kapitza had been trained as an electrical engineer and was a man of very strong personality and immense self-confidence. He impressed Rutherford with the need for applying the technique of electrical engineering to problems of physics, rather than relying on the old methods involving only apparatus put together by one or two pairs of hands, the apparatus that belonged to the days when Rutherford had said, "We've got no money, so we've got to think." Rutherford obtained for Kapitza a considerable grant of money from the Department of Scientific and Industrial Research, which was applied to build large-scale apparatus producing, for short periods—about a hundredth of a second—magnetic fields much more powerful than any that had hitherto been generated. With these fields Kapitza deflected the path of an alpha particle, as shown by the Wilson cloud track, considerably more than had hitherto been possible, and carried out many experiments on the magnetic properties of matter, with results of interest but not of fundamental importance.

Kapitza so much impressed Rutherford that he procured from the Department of Scientific and Industrial Research further large sums of money for the support of his work, and by his influence Kapitza was elected a Fellow of Trinity College in 1925 and a Fellow of the Royal Society in 1929. In the annual address which he delivered as President of the Royal Society in 1927 Rutherford devoted much of the time to Kapitza's work, saying, "The advance of science depends to a large extent on the development of new technical methods and their application to scientific problems." A special professorship was created for Kapitza and the Royal Society granted a large sum of money to build for him a special laboratory, called the Mond laboratory after the man who had made the bequest from which the funds were supplied. At the opening of this laboratory, in 1933, at which Stanley Baldwin, then chancellor of the University of Cambridge and Prime Minister of the United Kingdom, presided, Rutherford said, "The opening of this Laboratory is to me an important event. . . . I have taken an almost paternal interest in these new developments, but it is to the energy and enthusiasm of Professor Kapitza that we owe the forging of these new and powerful weapons of research which have added so materially to the possibilities of investigation in new fields at Cambridge."

It may be added that T. H. Laby, a physicist of distinction, has recorded that "There can be little doubt that there was a good deal of criticism in England of Kaptiza's appointment, probably more outside Cambridge than within." But, of course, those outside Cambridge knew only of his published work, which was not particularly impressive, and not of his stimulating personality.

In this laboratory Kapitza installed an elaborate plant for making liquid hydrogen and apparatus for making liquid helium, for the purpose of creating low temperatures at which to apply his high magnetic fields, probably with special objects in view. He was accustomed to go to his homeland from time to time, when he no doubt impressed the authorities with the facilities and reputation that he enjoyed in England. In any case, when he went to Russia in 1934 he was told that work of such importance as his should be carried out in his native country, which he was accordingly forbidden to leave. Rutherford wrote to Baldwin: "Kapitza was commandeered, as the Soviet authorities thought he was able to give important help to the electrical industry and they have not found out that they were misinformed." At any rate, as it was apparently considered that Kapitza's apparatus without Kapitza was of little use at Cambridge, arrangements were made to sell it to the Russian authorities at an agreed price of £30,000, very many times the money spent on the apparatus of all the research workers at Cambridge whose successes have been already discussed in this chapter and of Cockcroft and Walton, soon to be described. It cannot be said that any outstanding discovery had resulted from Kapitza's work up to the time of his departure, but the building of the new laboratory was an effect of his manifold activity.

COCKCROFT AND WALTON

At the end of the twenties a change was, then, gradually coming over the Cavendish. The work there was slowly moving from the old atmosphere of insignificant apparatus, designed with genius but made of bits of glass tube and sealing wax, scraps of zinc sulphide and such like, to large apparatus on the engineering scale, needing correspondingly more time to design and build and more money to pay for. Kapitza's work was the predominant and most costly example of the coming of the new type of installation, but it had no influence on the nuclear physics that was the main interest of the laboratory. However, the pioneering work of Cockcroft and Walton, which likewise employed the methods of electrical engineering, dealt with the disruption of the nucleus and so followed the tradition of Rutherford and Chadwick, although carried out on quite a different scale, with artificially accelerated particles instead of with the fast particles furnished by nature. It was the start of a new era in atomic transmutation.

John Cockcroft, born in 1897, went to Manchester University for two terms at the beginning of the great war of 1914–18, where he saw Rutherford and was greatly impressed. After the war, during which, as soon as he was old enough, he served at the front in the artillery, he trained with considerable success as an electrical engineer, but felt the attraction of physical research and went to Cambridge to work in the Cavendish, where he learned the elements of the laboratory arts under Appleton. After taking his Cambridge degree he duly settled down to research under Rutherford's direction and soon began to develop a scheme to disrupt nuclei with particles speeded up by application of a high voltage.

Rutherford was convinced that the attack on the nucleus was best conducted with energetic, that is, with swift, nuclei. The alpha particle, his pet projectile, had the advantage of possessing an energy equivalent to that which such a doubly charged particle would acquire under a potential difference of nearly four million volts. This was an impossibly high voltage in those distant days of 1930, while today potentials of thousands of millions of volts are generated in a number of installations scattered over the world. The alpha particle was, then, the obvious particle for nuclear attack. Unfortunately, the number of such particles from a reasonable source was not sufficient to produce many nuclear transmutations in a reasonable time. A tenth of a gram of radium, which is a large and expensive source, gives out several thousand million alpha particles per second, which sounds a prodigious number, but there is no way of bringing these particles, shot off in all directions, into a beam. Such a beam can only be produced by cutting off, that is, wasting, all the particles except those going within a small angle of a given direction, which is a relatively small fraction. Again, of these particles only about one in a million makes a bull's-eye hit, of the kind required to produce a transmutation, on the extremely small target offered by a nucleus.

On the other hand, particles can be produced in an electrical discharge tube in a restricted beam and in comparatively large quantities. A current of one ampere corresponds to about 6 million million million electronic charges passing per second, so that even a minute fraction of an ampere means a good supply of charged particles. The trouble was that, according to the theory prevailing in the twenties, an impinging particle could not penetrate the nucleus and produce a transmutation unless it had an energy corresponding to something like four million volts, because of what was called a potential barrier protecting the nucleus. At this time, there seemed no hope of producing such a potential in a discharge tube.

In 1928, however, G. Gamow, and R. W. Gurney in collaboration with E. U. Condon, showed independently that on the newly developed theory of wave mechanics there was a definite possibility that alpha particles of lower energy would penetrate the barrier and upset the nucleus. Cockcroft saw that the same arguments should apply to fast protons. The lower the energy, that is, the less the potential speeding up the bombarding particle, the smaller the chance of this penetration, but at some hundreds of thousands of volts the chance was quite good. It was as if there were a mountain ring protecting a treasure, with various tunnels through it, considerable in number at greater heights but getting fewer lower down, so that a man who had not sufficient energy to climb to the top still had a chance of finding his way through at a lower level, but a very small chance if his energy was too small to climb far up.

With Rutherford's benevolent encouragement Cockcroft, in collaboration with Walton, set to work on building a high energy installation of a type quite new to nuclear physics, to see if it would be possible to carry out nuclear transmutation with a stream of accelerated protons.

In Cockcroft and Walton's apparatus the alternating potential produced by an ordinary transformer was rectified and multiplied several times by an arrangement of two stacks of large condensers, now generally called capacitors, with a special instantaneous switching arrangement making use of an electronic device. The steady difference of potential so obtained, which ran up to about 500,000 volts, was applied to a long vertical tube, at the top of which hydrogen ions—protons—were produced by an ordinary electrical discharge. These protons were thus accelerated into a stream which could be used to strike any desired target at the bottom of the tubes. A general view of the apparatus is shown in Plate X, with Cockcroft at the observing end.

The construction would today be considered very crude. The rectifiers and the accelerator tube were built of glass cylinders about three feet long, taken from old-style petrol pumps then in common use in Britain. They were fastened together with flat metal plates and plasticene, the rectifier tube being about twelve feet high. There was, of course, a system of vacuum pumps, of a then recently invented type, so-called diffusion pumps. The cost of the total installation was very high, by the laboratory standards of the day, nearly £1000! The current conveyed by the discharge tube was getting on for a hundred-thousandth of an ampere, which meant about 50 million million protons per second, a wonderful supply of projectiles compared with those furnished by the beam from a radioactive source.

It should be mentioned that at about the same time E. O. Lawrence and M. S. Livingstone perfected in the United States a most ingenious way of multiplying voltage by a device called the cyclotron, which was later much used for nuclear experiments. The importance of this method was acknowledged by award of the Nobel Prize in Physics to E. O. Lawrence in 1939, "for the discovery and development of the cyclotron and for the results obtained by its aid, especially with regard to artificially radioactive elements." It need hardly be said that since Cockcroft and Walton's pioneering work, particle accelerators, as installations for producing rapid nuclear particles and electrons are called, have been enormously developed, so that the original apparatus seems today rather like an ingenious toy. But work of prime importance was carried out with it, work which showed the way to the fantastic performances of the present time.

Cockcroft and Walton directed their hail of swift protons onto a lithium target. To detect the alpha particles which they hoped to produce from it, they used the good old zinc sulphide screen and low-power micro-

scope, Rutherford's well-tried method. They soon observed scintillations characteristic of alpha particles and,
needless to say, at once called in Rutherford to see the
minute telltale flashes. They then set a thin lithium target obliquely across the beam, so that particles could
be observed on opposite sides, by Cockcroft on one
side and Walton on the other. They had a paper recorder with two pens, each worked by a separate key,
Cockcroft having one key and Walton the other. Each
pressed his key when he observed a scintillation. The
two signals always occurred at the same time, so that it
convincingly appeared that the alphas were emitted in
pairs.

This investigation showed clearly that what had happened was that the lithium nucleus, mass 7 and charge
3, had, by the impact of a proton, mass 1 and charge
1, been split into two alpha particles, each of mass 4
and charge 2: $4 \times 2 = 7 + 1; 2 \times 2 = 3 + 1$. But it
also appeared that the alphas were thrown off with
great energy, with an energy greater than that of the
impinging proton. This was a consequence of the fact
that a very small amount of mass was lost in the transmutation: the lithium 7 has not mass exactly 7 nor the
hydrogen mass exactly 1 nor the helium mass exactly 4
units. It was Aston, the isotope king, who was responsible for the precise measurements of the atomic masses
that were involved in these considerations. When the
exact figures are used it appears that it is about a quarter of a per cent of the mass that disappears. Now Einstein had demonstrated that mass and energy were
equivalent, in the same way that heat and work are
equivalent. Very little mass is equivalent to a great deal
of energy: one gram, roughly one twenty-eighth of an
ounce, is equivalent to a million horsepower for thirty-
three hours! The extra energy of the alpha particles,

when allowance was made for the energy of the proton, exactly corresponded to the loss of mass, thus furnishing a valuable confirmation of Einstein's relation, which comes in everywhere in the modern generation of power by nuclear reactions. Of course, in all ordinary chemical reactions there is no measurable change of mass. An appreciable conversion of mass into energy can be produced by nuclear reactions only.

As soon as it had been established that such comparatively low voltages were adequate to disrupt nuclei, Marcus Oliphant and Rutherford, later aided by B. B. Kinsey, set to work to devise an apparatus to produce not a higher voltage, but a much more abundant supply of particles, of fixed energy, not only protons, but also deuterons, nuclei of heavy hydrogen. With these they effected many nuclear transformations of great interest. The artificial transmutation of the elements was now a regular laboratory job.

Cockcroft and Walton's results were obtained by counting methods: the other great Cavendish method of studying flying particles, the Wilson cloud chamber, was soon involved. With photographs of ray tracks, of measured length and direction, the earlier transformations were soon confirmed, and others were investigated. A photograph by P. I. Dee and Walton, showing the rapid alpha particles produced by bombarding lithium with protons, the Cockcroft-Walton reaction, is reproduced in Plate XII. The four bundles of track are due to the fact that the alpha particles issue from the high vacuum discharge tube into the air of the chamber through the very thin mica windows of a four-sided cage.

FERMI AND TRANSMUTATION BY NEUTRONS

In 1933 a new phenomenon of great interest to Rutherford was discovered: isotopes that were radioactive were artificially made. The Joliot-Curies found that by bombarding light elements, such as boron, magnesium, and aluminum, with alpha particles, such isotopes were produced, some of which gave out positrons in the course of their rather rapid decay, a new feature. Immediately afterward the Italian Enrico Fermi, whose name was destined to become widely known for his work in Chicago on the atomic pile that led to the atomic bomb, made a further sensational discovery in this field. He and his collaborators, working in Italy, first of all made a detailed investigation of the manufacture of artificial radioactive elements by bombarding stable elements with neutrons. With the source available to them, a small glass bulb containing radon and beryllium powder, the number of neutrons emitted is small as these things go—only a few tens of millions per second—but they have a long range and enter nuclei with ease, since they are not repelled as charged particles are. This ability to penetrate is of special importance when heavy elements, with large nuclear charges, are concerned, since these repel alphas so strongly that they cannot get near enough to produce any disintegration.

This special effectiveness of neutrons was realized by Fermi, who with his collaborators produced, out of sixty-three elements investigated, thirty-seven new elements showing radioactive qualities, a pretty wholesale manufacture. Among these were new elements produced from thorium and uranium, which were heavier than any natural elements. They were radioactive in a different way, for whereas natural thorium and uranium spontaneously give out alpha particles, the elements formed from them by the neutrons gave out beta particles, that is, electrons. Still more remarkable, perhaps, Fermi and his collaborators found, as a result of a chance observation, that neutrons which had been slowed down by repeatedly hitting protons, which have the same mass, were much more effective in producing atomic transmutations than fast neutrons. Protons, of course, as has been pointed out, occur in quantity as the nuclei of the hydrogen atoms closely packed in paraffin wax. With medical applications in mind, they took out a patent for the process. They had no thought of releasing nuclear energy for bombs or industrial uses to which the process was later applied. It was not until some years after Rutherford's death that the famous "pile" in the disused squash court in Chicago produced heat in appreciable quantity from nuclear reaction. The date, December 2, 1942, when the pile was first successfully put into action marked a new period in man's control over nature, which, like the invention of the internal-combustion engine, involved immense possibilities of industrial progress and immense danger of destruction. But that is another story.

Connected with Fermi in this work were E. Amaldi, O. D'Agostino, B. Pontecorvo, F. Rasetti and E. Segré. Rutherford's interest, and their immediate resort to him, is shown by the fact that he communicated to the Royal Society for publication in its *Proceedings* the two papers, printed in 1934 and 1935, that first made the full results known to the world, although short preliminary reports had been published in Italian. At the end of the second paper results for fifty-nine elements are discussed. Making elements with new nuclear masses, which broke down radioactively into stable elements, had become a commonplace. In 1938 the Nobel Prize was awarded to Fermi, and in the same year, in consequence of Mussolini's adoption of the Nazi code, the Fermi family left Italy for the United States. The story of Fermi's life is told in a fascinating and most humorous way in his wife's book *Atoms in the Family*, published after his death.

Rutherford was naturally very much interested in the early work of Fermi on the disintegration produced by slow neutrons. In a lecture delivered two years before Fermi's great discovery he had asserted that the peculiar properties of the neutron allowed it to "approach closely, or even to enter, nuclei of high atomic number" and had anticipated that it would "prove an effective agent in extending our knowledge of the artificial disintegration of the elements." He wrote to me on November 17, 1936, less than a year before his death, "Within a month of Chadwick's proof of the neutron, Feather in the Cavendish showed by expansion chamber work that neutrons were very effective in disintegrating both oxygen and nitrogen, and this was followed up by Harkins in the U.S.A. The main merit of Fermi was his rapid trial whether neutrons would produce radioactive bodies immediately after the Curie-Joliot discovery."

LECTURES AND MEETINGS

It is clear, then, that the years 1932 to 1934 were a wonderful period for advances in nuclear science. They saw the discovery of the neutron and of the positron, the transmutation of atoms by particles artificially accelerated to high energies, the artificial manufacture of new radioactive atoms and of atoms of higher atomic weight than any found in nature. The science of nuclear disintegration and combination was already entering a lusty childhood and the father, Rutherford, was naturally taking the greatest interest in all the new developments, both in the Cavendish and abroad. He was not so actively concerned with the work of the laboratory, with suggesting and supervising experiments, as he had been, no doubt because much of his time was occupied with a diversity of tasks which his great fame and position involved. For one thing, he was much called upon to deliver important lectures, of the kind already mentioned, for which his theme was, in general, some aspect of nuclear transmutation. He was an outstanding speaker on any subject in which he was passionately interested. He would often start in a somewhat hesitating manner, repeating phrases, and, as it were, feeling his way, but as soon as he warmed up and his enthusiasm took control, he was clear and enthralling, full of fire and inspiration. He always used plain language and possessed the power of simplifying any nuclear matter with which he was dealing.

Typical lectures, given in commemoration of great names, were the Boyle lecture given at Oxford in 1933; the Mendeléeff lecture, given to commemorate the centenary of the birth of that great chemist, Dmitri Ivanovitch Mendeléeff, and the Ludwig Mond lecture given at his old haunt, Manchester, both in 1934; the series of John Joly memorial lectures, given in Dublin in 1935 to celebrate the achievements of an outstanding Irish scientist, a friend who, among other things, had been the first to point out the geological significance of the heat evolved by the radioactive elements contained in the earth; the James Watt lecture, delivered in Watt's birthplace in Scotland, to mark the two-hundredth anniversary of the birth of the inventor of the modern steam engine; and the Faraday lecture to the Chemical

Society, both of the latter in 1936. In all these discourses he dealt with different aspects of radioactivity and nuclear transmutation, but always without obtruding his own work, which he often cited without saying who was responsible for it. The last lecture of this character that he gave was the Henry Sidgwick memorial lecture at the end of 1936, which is worthy of mention because on it was based his little book *The Newer Alchemy*, to which reference has already been made. This book gives an admirable account of nuclear transmutation as it was at the end of his life.

Another task that fell to him was in connection with the great International Conference on Physics held in London in 1934 under the auspices of the Royal Society, which was attended by a great array of distinguished physicists from many lands. As well as the meetings in London, a special meeting was, by Rutherford's invitation, held at Cambridge. The international character of the meeting is well illustrated by the fact that an Italian, speaking in French, gave to the predominantly English-speaking audience an account of recent work carried out by a German who was unable to attend. Three days were devoted to nuclear matters, as a preliminary to which Rutherford gave the opening address. This was a brilliant exposition of the early history, summarizing the work of Bohr, Moseley, Aston, Geiger and Marsden, and the others, followed by an account of the researches into the transmutation of elements, in which he laid stress upon the then recent work of Fermi. His last lecture of this kind was prepared for an address to be delivered in India at a joint meeting of the Indian Science Congress and the British Association for the Advancement of Science, of which he had been chosen to be president. He died, however, before this meeting, which took place in January 1938, and his address, which had been written out, was delivered by Sir James Jeans, who became president on Rutherford's death. This carefully prepared speech is remarkable for the fact that in the first half he dealt with Indian affairs, emphasizing, for instance, the importance for India of research on foodstuffs, while in the second half he turned to his usual theme, the "age-old problem of the transmutation of matter." Personally, I have little doubt that if he himself had delivered the lecture the audience would have noted a sudden transition from a well-reasoned but not particularly stirring speech, delivered with a certain consultation of notes, to an enthusiastic and spontaneous description of the work that was nearest to his heart.

Needless to say, Rutherford was called on to give many other addresses. For instance, once a year he delivered a discourse at the Royal Institution, dealing with some recent advance in nuclear physics and usually illustrated with experiments, and he opened laboratories and proposed toasts at great official banquets, always very effectively.

A matter dear to Rutherford's warm heart was the work of the Academic Assistance Council. The coming into full and unlimited power of Hitler in Germany in 1934 had been followed by a general expulsion of Jewish, or even remotely non-Aryan, persons from all German universities and such institutions, and in consequence there were in England a great number of German refugees, many of very high scientific standing. In 1933 Rutherford took the chair at a great meeting, where ten thousand people were present, called to consider the problem of the relief of these men, many of them without money or possessions. After Rutherford had depicted the situation and Albert Einstein and Sir Austen Chamberlain, a prominent political figure, had spoken, the appeal for funds for the newly founded Academic Assistance Council, of which Rutherford became president, was launched. Rutherford in private held the strong views that one would expect about the Nazi behavior. "I found him in a state of explosive indignation at the treatment that was being meted out in Germany to scientific colleagues," wrote Sir William Beveridge, who was himself very active in Assistance Council matters. In public, however, Rutherford insisted on the necessity of nonpolitical action, although, "Each of us may have his own private political views." Rutherford was very active on behalf of the council, of which the name was changed in 1935 to the Society for the Protection of Science and Learning, and his fame and forthrightness did much for its success. In 1936 he reported that conditions had recently become much worse in Germany. To this humane work he devoted much attention, with excellent results. Many of the German physicists who were aided by the society afterward became professors at British universities.

Another great activity in which he was much involved was the Department of Scientific and Industrial Research, created in 1915 by the government to encourage and support financially investigations in both pure and applied science. One function, for instance, is the provision of scholarships for promising research students. In 1930 Rutherford was appointed chairman of the Advisory Council of the Department, an office which he continued to hold until his death. He devoted much attention to his duties in this connection, for he never undertook an office lightly. This position brought him into contact with the world of industrial science and added to the calls upon him to speak on such occasions as the opening of new industrial laboratories. He also spoke occasionally in the House of Lords, of which his elevation to the peerage had made him a member, on scientific matters, for instance on the application of research to the rubber industry. All these odd examples have been given to show how much, during the last years of his life, Rutherford was involved in matters that took him out of the laboratory, which in his Manchester days he practically never left. Then he had nothing to think about but physics; now some new task, which he felt it his duty to undertake, was always arising. It is not suggested that he did not enjoy being a public figure, but, well as he acquitted himself, he could not develop for his public functions the same overmastering enthusiasm, the same vivid qualities of leadership, that research called forth.

Marcus Oliphant

With the research work of Rutherford's last years Marcus Oliphant was much associated. Oliphant, who was born at Adelaide, Australia, in 1901—the same year as Fermi and Lawrence of the cyclotron—had come to Cambridge in 1927. Reference has already been made to the striking work which he carried out with Rutherford on the disruption of the nucleus by a copious supply of particles of comparatively low energy, just after the pioneering work of Cockcroft and Walton. Rutherford, Oliphant, and P. Harteck employed nuclei of heavy hydrogen, deuterons, as bombarding particles and as one target used deuterium, in the form of a solid compound so as to have plenty of atoms in a small space. Chemically, of course, deuterium behaves exactly like ordinary hydrogen. As a result of this shooting deuterons onto deuterons, they obtained a new isotope of hydrogen, of mass 3 units; the two reacting nuclei, each of mass 2 units, and charge 1 unit, gave a nucleus of mass 3 and a nucleus of mass 1, the latter being an ordinary proton. The new 3 isotope of hydrogen was called tritium and its nucleus the triton. This triton was subsequently shown to be unstable, breaking down, in a radioactive manner, into a new isotope of helium, of mass 3 units, and an ordinary electron. The loss of this 1 unit of negative charge, of course, puts the positive nuclear charge up by 1, so that hydrogen changes into helium. To explain the transformations is all simple arithmetic of charge units and mass units; to produce the transformations is not quite so simple.

Oliphant, who was Rutherford's right-hand man during his last few years at the Cavendish, with the title of assistant director of research, was just about to take up the professorship of physics at Birmingham at the time of Rutherford's death. In 1950 he went to Australia as the director of the Research School of Physical Sciences at the Australian National University. There he designed and erected a huge installation for accelerating protons to an energy expressed by ten thousand million volts. In a way this is a continuance of the Rutherford tradition, use of energetic nuclei for smashing other nuclei, but the energy in question is about a thousand times as great as that of the alpha particle.

Rutherford's last scientific paper, on work carried out in conjunction with Oliphant and A. R. Kempton, was published by the Royal Society in 1935 and was further concerned with nuclear transformations produced in beryllium and boron by bombardment with protons and deuterons. Thus he remained devoted to simple nuclear transformations, the study of which he had initiated, until the end. He was, for instance, very pleased when Dee and Gilbert showed, with the Wilson cloud chamber, how a boron nucleus—mass 11 units, nuclear charge 5 units—under proton bombardment could be split into 3 alpha particles—good old alpha particles, and 3 of them from one hit! Once more, the arithmetic is quite simple: the addition of the 1 unit of mass and 1 unit of charge of the proton makes total mass 12 and total charge 6, which is sufficient for 3 particles each of nuclear mass 4 units and nuclear charge 2 units.

UNEXPECTED DEATH

Thus in the last few years of his life Rutherford was still personally concerned with research, but much less actively than he had been in the Manchester days and the early years at the Cavendish. It is clear from what has been said that for a considerable period he had become more and more engaged with matters that, although concerned with science, lay outside the research laboratory which had once been his beloved home, as expressed by his exclamation, already quoted, "Robinson, you know, I *am* sorry for the poor fellows that haven't got labs. to work in." It appeared, too, that in spite of his prodigious natural vigor and energy he was becoming tired. He had built a country cottage for a "holiday home" and spoke of retiring when he reached the age of seventy, which would be in 1941. On the death of his old Manchester friend Horace Lamb, a famous mathematician, at the end of 1934, he had written that Lamb was "one of the few men that grew old gracefully. So many are inclined to hang on and to grasp for power when they ought to be dandling their grandchildren." It seems probable, then, that he contemplated gradually easing off his work and making way for a successor. But it was not to be.

The end was sad and sudden. On September 5, 1937,

Rutherford wrote to Geiger, in the best of spirits, thanking him for a letter of congratulation on his sixty-sixth birthday and saying that he proposed to have a month of good rest before going off on his tour of India. A month later he wrote to his old friend of McGill days, Eve, from his country cottage, saying, after some words about radioactive sources and cyclotrons, "I have made a still further clearance of the blackberry patch and the view is now quite attractive," which shows him in vigorous health. His death was brought about by similar work in the garden, in this case that of his Cambridge house. He was cutting down the branch of a tree when he had a nasty fall, which resulted in an abdominal derangement, which at first did not seem serious. His wife sent for a masseur, who gave him manipulative treatment. However, the next day, feeling really unwell, he sent for his doctor. He was taken to a nursing home and there an operation was performed by an eminent surgeon, with what at first appeared to be good results. The day after, alas, things rapidly became worse and all that could be done was to alleviate his pain. Among his last words to his wife were, "I want to leave a hundred pounds to Nelson College. You can see to it." His old school, for which he bore so much affection, was in his mind at the end. He died on October 19, within six days of his first sympton of distress. For a man of his heavy build it appears that the kind of intestinal derangement from which he suffered is more serious than for those of slighter structure.

It need hardly be said that the entirely unexpected death of the great and genial leader gave rise to very sincere and widespread distress. Not only was everyone in scientific circles talking of it with keenest regret, but the newspapers gave it much attention and there was a national feeling of loss. This found official expression when a proposal made by Sir Frank Smith that he should be buried in Westminster Abbey was at once granted. The Abbey is the most celebrated church in the British Empire, where all the sovereigns are crowned, royal marriages take place, and until 1760 many of the kings and queens of England were buried. The graves of many of the country's most celebrated men are there: writers such as Samuel Johnson and Macaulay are buried there; poets from Chaucer to Tennyson have their resting place in an angle known as the Poets' Corner; and mighty men of science, including such figures as Isaac Newton, John Herschel, Charles Darwin, and Lord Kelvin have their tombs there. Burial in Westminster Abbey is thus a sign of the greatest national respect. Rutherford's ashes were interred close to Newton's tomb, in the presence of a full and distinguished congregation.

THE FATHER OF NUCLEAR SCIENCE

It is certain that Rutherford is one of the greatest figures in the history of science. He is responsible for the modern belief that the atom, far from being a stable structure, is capable of changes of fundamental significance, in some cases spontaneous, in other cases provoked by means that he was the first to devise. Let us, before saying farewell to him, consider briefly some of his outstanding characteristics.

He was essentially an experimenter, with a tendency to mistrust any theory involving conceptions of which he could not form a clear mental image. The alpha particles and other particles with which he dealt so intimately were as real to him as the ball is to the baseball player; he saw them in their flight and encounters as clearly in his mind as the veteran spectator sees the happenings of a match that he is recalling. I remember a discussion after dinner about the philosophy of physics when the great astronomer and theorist Sir Arthur Eddington said that possibly electrons were only mental concepts and had no real existence. Whereupon Rutherford got up and, with the air of one saying "You have insulted the woman I love," exclaimed, "Not exist? Not exist? Why I can see them as plainly as I can see that spoon in front of me," pointing to the article of tableware. For abstruse conceptions like the theory of relativity he had little taste. It is recorded that the famous German physicist Willy Wien said to him in 1910, a few years after Einstein had first put forward the theory, "But no Anglo-Saxon can understand relativity!" to which Rutherford replied laughingly, "No! they have too much sense." Of the theory of wave mechanics, which from 1925 onward had had a series of successes, he said in 1934, "The theory of wave-mechanics, however bizarre it may appear—and it is so in some respects —has the astonishing virtue that it works . . . ," a somewhat grudging acknowledgment of its triumphs. He always had a jesting and pretended hostility to the theorists, well expressed in his answer to the suggestion that he should choose for the title of his address in South Africa "The Trend of Modern Physics." The reply was, "The trend of modern physics? I can't give a paper on that. It would only take two minutes. All I could say would be that the theoretical physicists have got their tails up and it is time that we experimentalists pulled them down again!" It was probably the development of wave mechanics that he had in mind. Again, his friend Eve said of these developments that much of them left him unmoved, although he was ready to avail himself of any conclusions which helped the investigations in which he was interested. He said jokingly of the theorists, "They play games with their symbols, but we, in the Cavendish, turn out the real solid facts of Nature." His own words have been much quoted here because they are characteristic, not only of his attitude but also of the way he was wont to express himself; they help to picture the man, especially if the reader imagines them said in a loud, boisterous voice, half seriously, half with a smile.

Rutherford was a man of extraordinary scientific foresight, as instanced particularly in his anticipation of the neutron and of the isotopes of hydrogen and helium. It is sometimes asked if Rutherford foresaw, as a result of his work, the atomic bomb and the wholesale release of nuclear energy in general. In a lecture given in 1936, the year before he died, he referred to the possibility of obtaining energy on an industrial scale (he did not speak, or apparently think, of a bomb) from nuclear transmutation, saying, "While the over-all efficiency of the process rises with increase of energy of the bombarding particle, there seems to be little hope of gaining useful energy from the atoms by such methods. On the other hand, the recent discovery of the neutron and the proof of its extraordinary effectiveness in producing transmutations at very low velocities opens up new possibilities, if only a method could be found of producing slow neutrons in quantity with little expenditure of energy. At the moment, however, the natural radioactive bodies are the only known source for generating energy from atomic nuclei, but this is on far too small a scale to be useful for technical purposes." In his little book *The Newer Alchemy,* published in the following year, he said much the same, adding, "The outlook for gaining useful energy from the atoms by artificial processes of transformation does not look very promising." He did not, then, contemplate the possibility of any planned large-scale release of atomic energy in the near future, although, being Rutherford, he naturally put his finger upon the essential point, the release of neutrons in quantity. It was his old student of the McGill days, Otto Hahn, who two years later showed how the uranium nucleus could be split, with just such a release of neutrons, a discovery which, together with Fermi's work, was to lead in the course of a few years to the atomic bomb. In connection with this terrible consequence of his own work on the nucleus another utterance of Rutherford's at about the same time seems appropriate: "I am doubtful, however, whether the most imaginative scientific man, except in rare cases, is able to foresee the result of any discovery."

A characteristic of his genius was that Rutherford seemed to know by instinct what observations were important and what were relatively trivial. Many people seem to think that great scientific discoveries are due to stringent sequences of logical thought, leading inexorably from one conclusion to another. They are more often due to some chance observation, recognized as significant by a kind of instinct, following on long and intense preoccupation with a particular subject. The famous German professor Friedrich Wilhelm Kohlrausch said of Faraday, "He smells the truth," and the same might be said of Rutherford. The fact that a few alpha particles were observed to be scattered through an unexpectedly large angle might have been some triviality, might have been a spurious effect due to some chance radioactive contamination. Anyhow the scattering of alpha particles might not have been a matter that deserved prolonged attention. Rutherford saw that the large-angle scattering was of profound importance and, as a result of always having the subject in his mind, conceived the nuclear structure of the atom.

Isaac Newton, when asked how he made his discoveries, said, "By always thinking unto them," and, on another occasion, "I keep the subject constantly before me and wait until the first dawnings open little by little into the full light." Rutherford was in character and personality totally unlike Newton, but he could have said the same thing (and, if an interpolation may be pardoned, one of the troubles of professors engaged on research nowadays is that very very few of them can say it. The administrators see to that). Artificial transmutation of the elements was one of the subjects that he kept constantly before him; I remember hearing him speak of it in 1914, but it was in 1919 that, as has been described, he first effected such a transmutation.

In person he was a big burly man, with a loud voice to which reference has more than once been made—it was a characteristic. When a friend of his was told that he intended to speak by radio from Cambridge, England, to Harvard he asked, "Why use radio?" He looked something like a successful farmer, except for his piercing eyes, which had a curious fascination, and his great breadth of forehead. The informal photograph in Plate XI, taken at the back of the Cavendish Laboratory in 1934, gives an excellent impression of the man toward the end of his life. He was quite without affectation, self-consciousness, or pretentiousness of any kind. He was essentially kindly, but he was quite outspoken and not always in a good temper. On his bad days he was irascible and storms might blow up suddenly. As Niels Bohr, looking back, said vividly, to those in his laboratory it was often as if the sun suddenly began to shine when he arrived in the morning, but sometimes it was as if the sky was darkened by a thundercloud. His fits of bad temper, however, did not last long and often gave way to a laugh if the man on whom he was venting his troubled mood stood up to him and answered back. In accordance with his simplicity of character he gave free expression to his feelings at the moment. He was completely honest and straightforward and nobody ever bore a grudge against him for occasional roughness. It can be truthfully said of him, as of very few people, that he had no enemies. He was a great leader, who had a wonderful way of winning the affection of his collaborators, as well as inspiring them.

A massive simplicity, an unsophisticated greatness characterized the man, whose name will endure as long as our civilization lasts. Referring to his odes, the poet Horace wrote, *Exegi monumentum aere perennius*—I have erected a monument which will last longer than bronze. Rutherford could have said the same of his work.

INDEX